BODY
PEACE

RELEASE SHAME AND
DISCOVER BODY FREEDOM

Published By:

www.PromotingNaturalHealth.com

BODY
PEACE

RELEASE SHAME AND
DISCOVER BODY FREEDOM

BODYPeace:
Release Shame and Discover Body Freedom
By Kasey Arena and Heather Waxman

To contact the publisher, visit
www.PromotingNaturalHealth.com

Printed in the United States of America
ISBN-10: 0990646211
ISBN-13: 978-0-9906462-1-1

This book is dedicated to girls and women everywhere
who are struggling to find their own
#BODYpeace. This is for you, sisters.
You are beautiful. We love you.

Table of Contents

Welcome to BODYpeace

Welcome to your BODYpeace journey, sister!

We are so psyched you have made this amazing commitment to yourself. Before we dive into what your BODYpeace journey is all about, we want to take some time to give you the scoop on who we are, how we found BODYpeace, and what qualifies us to guide you along this transformational journey. We hope you can see and feel pieces of yourself in our stories and use those pieces, day by day, as inspiration to put yourself back together again.

Okay, here goes!

Both of us have been through the ringer when it comes to our relationships with food and our bodies. We've had our fair share of health scares, fainting episodes, and compulsive food issues. We've obsessively counted calories, restricted ourselves to cookie cutter food regimens, and tried to mold our bodies into a certain shape, thinking that would bring us true happiness. Instead, it brought us to our knees with severe cases of BODYshame. We longed for BODYfreedom.

When we'd had enough of the BODYshame spiral, we each had our very own surrender moments and decided to change our destructive ways. It wasn't easy. It was uncomfortable, and there were quite a few relapses along the way. But we wouldn't trade one second of any of it. Why? Because our eating disorders paved the way for us to follow our purpose - to help you discover your own BODYpeace. That is something we wouldn't change for anything.

We wrote our stories for you with the intention of helping you feel connected to us and supported by us. We hope these two journeys can inspire you to own your BODYpeace journey and help you know that you, too, have a purpose that is awakening inside of you. This purpose will continue to reveal itself to you throughout the next thirty days.

Stay lovely and be true to you,

Heather & Kasey

Heather's Story

"Your whole life, you've been starving yourself to feed others." The astrologer was so right - both literally and figuratively speaking. After chatting with me for just one hour, Nancy was able to hone in on what I'd been trying to put into words my entire life. With ten words, she'd summed up how I had chosen to live my life for nearly twenty-three years. I'd never felt so seen and heard until that moment. And that small yet pivotal moment sparked something inside of me.

I believe our lives are pre-destined - that our gorgeous souls cut a deal with the Universe before making their way into being here on Earth. At the very core of our being is a strong desire to grow and evolve, and that's why our souls come here. It's almost as if your soul says, "These are the lessons I am here to learn, and these are the things I want to accomplish." You come here, to this Earth school, and become the student of your unique life experience. I know with every fiber of my being that my soul chose to come here to learn this - to transform my BODYshame into BODYpeace and, learn to nourish my truth instead of starving it.

Tracing the dots and connecting them backward, it's very clear to me that I was destined to have an eating disorder.

Before I was born, my parents were blessed with a beautiful baby girl named Katie. She lived for three days before passing away from a rare heart defect. Two years later, I came along. My mom still hadn't fully grieved the death of my sister. She felt guilty, and ashamed, and like she could have done something more, or something better, to prevent her passing. She carried this burden with her into her pregnancy with me, along with a case of Orthorexia, a disorder in which you're obsessed with eating only "healthy" foods. My mom was so scared of losing me too. She wanted to have the most perfect pregnancy to make sure nothing happened to me. So she turned to food. She knew she could control what she ate and, if she ate "perfectly," she thought that would ensure I would survive the pregnancy and be healthy.

As far back as I can remember, I always carried this underlying sense of guilt and shame within me. I was the mini queen of "I'm sorry," and I apologized for things all the time - even seemingly innocent things like dropping a fork on the kitchen floor. I also had this overwhelming desire to be the perfect daughter and have the perfect family. These "truths" were instilled in me before birth and, without questioning what my own truths were I chased after them, believing they were the key to making me feel complete. I subconsciously believed that the more perfect a daughter I was, the less pain my mother would feel over losing my sister, the happier she would be, and the happier I would be.

By age sixteen, I had taken my quest for perfection to new heights. After a girl in high school called me chubby, I started obsessively counting calories and over-exercising. In just two months, I whittled myself down to 109 pounds, a dangerous weight for my 5'8'' frame. I continued to starve myself physically and emotionally, always making choices that would make my parents happy. It didn't even occur to me to check in with myself first because, in my mind, the only option was the one that would make them happiest.

So when I got to college, I started studying nutrition. I had no intentions of becoming a registered dietician - I just wanted to help people who were going through what I was going through. Even though I wasn't healed, I had this overwhelming desire to inspire people and help them work through their own disordered eating patterns. In response to that inner calling, I started a healthy living blog where I chronicled my daily meals and fitness routine. The whole time I did it, I felt like a total fraud. I wasn't ready to come clean about what was really going on behind the scenes in my life because it was such a total mess. My blog became a safe haven - an escape from the inner and outer hell I was dealing with. As I watched my mother fall prey to alcoholism and my parents' marriage disintegrate, I felt truly alone.

When you cling to things that are not serving your highest good and don't make the move to switch gears, the Universe tends to rip them away from you. Everything I had tried to do my whole life - to keep my perfect family together - was ripped away from me. I didn't know who I was apart from my family. The Universe was saying to me, "Here's a blank canvas. Now, paint what you really want to paint on it." It was time to live my life for me - not live the life I thought my parents wanted me to live.

In 2013, I wiped my blog clean and completely started over. I came out of the spiritual closet, released a meditation album, and started to come clean about my ~~recovery~~ discovery journey from my eating disorder. I started to let my true self shine. I let myself be the nurturing, sensitive chick that I am (with a hint of sass) and let the Universe take the wheel and show me how to heal. My spiritual healing journey took me further than I'd ever gotten with any of the multiple therapists and doctors I saw. For the first time in my life, I finally felt at home in my body. Now, here I am, less than two years later, and it feels like I've been living in a daydream, awakening to my truth one "yes" at a time.

Left: Here I am at my lowest weight in 2008. My hair was thin and falling out, my BMI was at a 16, and I lost my period. I was depressed, partying like crazy on the weekends, and felt so disconnected from everything and everyone.

Right: Here I am six years later. This girl has found a home in her body. She's proudly gained twenty pounds, a period, and has a full head of hair.

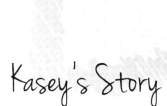

Kasey's Story

"We're moving."

These dreaded words marked the beginning of a downward spiral towards losing myself, and ultimately what helped me find myself.

You see, one day after fourth grade, I got off the bus and headed to the comforting little house we grew up in. I never thought a step through my front door would lead to a conversation about a decision my parents had already made. We were moving. It wasn't like we decided to get up and move to a different state…we literally moved about four minutes down the road, but it sure felt like we were leaving the country. My fourth-grade mind could not understand this, and my life quickly felt out of control.

So, I turned to the only thing in life I felt I COULD control - food (or so I thought).

In order to feel in control of something, I started to slowly eliminate foods from my "approved" list in my head, not to lose weight, but keep myself from feeling "sick."

These rules then boiled down to my diet consisting of mainly nothing. I wanted control. Without even realizing it, I was spiraling down this path of rules and regulations I was putting on myself without recognizing my rapid weight loss happening at the same time.

And when I did eat, I liked control. I liked controlling the fact that I PICKED when I ate. Every four hours, like clockwork, I would "allow myself" to eat another meal. And guess what, I got an adrenaline rush whenever that clock would hit four hours because I knew I was "allowed" to eat, and it gave me a great feeling.

Despite always wanting to be in control, I actually started to lose control of who I was at the same time because I was so numb to all the calorie counting and restrictions. I felt sad, depressed, and alone. No one knew how to help me - my parents, my friends, not even me. I was at a loss.

I vividly remember sitting in my room, desperate for an answer. I prayed to God and hoped that I wouldn't have to live or feel like this forever.

The feeling of "no control" over the situation was, deep down, what I was dealing with, not the fear of being sick. This concept of "fear of losing control" was something I worked on for years in therapy and still struggle with to this day.

At eleven years old, anxiety forced me to grow up quickly and understand concepts that most fifth graders were not even aware of. Through years of therapy and self-work, I started to heal - slowly but surely. Without therapy, I don't think I'd be as far along as I am today. I had to struggle to find my strength and to ultimately help others from past experiences.

Anxiety disorders never truly go away one hundred percent, but you CAN learn how to handle and manage them over the years. Change happens, and instead of freaking out over it, I embrace it and have faith that God has led me down this path for a reason.

And now, I've come a long, long way from that anxiety ridden fifth grader I once was. I am now a proud woman who wants to help others realize they are NOT ALONE in their journeys.

Yes, I grew up quickly and at a young age, but I wouldn't change anything about that. I never liked talking about the issues, but once I did, it was like the weight of the world was off my shoulders. My motto, "BE TRUE TO YOU," is something I so strongly believe in - I am me, not you. You are you, not me. BE YOURSELF and be proud of where you come from and where you are going. Don't judge others' stories, and accept their differences. Accepting and actually acknowledging the anxiety out loud will help you get through it. You've got to accept it to move forward.

Can we control everything that happens to us? Hell no. But we sure can have faith in ourselves to follow the road we're meant to drive down. So as we take this journey together, let's work on less judgment, more acceptance, and finding that BODYpeace within ourselves - no matter the struggles we face.

Our Story

When it comes to our journey, we are truly the yin and yang of BODYpeace. Kasey's approach is high-energy and amped up while Heather's is powerful in a softer and gentler way. Heather's mission is to help you awaken to your own magnificence and transform your pain into peace. Kasey's mission is to help you use food and fitness as tools for you to love your body instead of tools to fit into a certain mold or extreme.

Throughout our journey, we realized that not only was it important to share our own stories, but it was equally as important to join forces with like-minded soul sisters who really got us. That's why we bonded so quickly. We both endured similar struggles and, as we entered the maintenance phase of our ~~recovery~~ discovery journeys, we knew that support was more important than ever. We shared our nuggets of wisdom with one another and checked in with each other regularly. We got the connection and support we needed while still being able to be the kick-ass independent women that we are.

It is our mission to take these nuggets of wisdom we have learned during our BODYpeace journeys and give them to you so you too can release your secret shame and discover the BODYfreedom that has been in you all along. We also wanted to come together to bring you your very own BODYpeace community so you can feel supported, connected, and inspired throughout your entire journey.

What is BODYpeace?

Defining BODYpeace

Before you dive into your BODYpeace journey, we want to give you the BODYpeace commandments. Consider this your BODYpeace ammunition to prime you for your journey!

WHAT BODYpeace IS...

A transformational experience and a guide for the modern day soul sister (that's you!). We promise that if you put 100% of your effort into this journey, you will be guided to fall in love with your body - FOR REAL.

A support system. Not only do you have exclusive access to the BODYpeace community, but we are energetically supporting you every step of the way. Sound trippy? That's okay…just trust us.

A guidebook. That's right. This is a guidebook - not a bible. If something doesn't resonate with you, feel free to skip it. However, if you simply feel resistance to doing something, DO IT! Your ego really wants to keep you in the dark and wants you to stay stuck in your BODYshame spiral. So, it will try to tell you to resist doing certain exercises that, deep down, you know your soul is calling you to do. DON'T SKIP THOSE! The things we resist the most are often the things we need the most.

A safe haven. You can return to BODYpeace over and over again. Every time you go through this journey, you will receive a new insight and new shifts. That is the miracle of evolving your soul!

A supportive community. We are ALL in this together. No shame is welcome here and no judgments are EVER gonna go down. We support, we guide, and we nurture. Deal?

WHAT BODYpeace IS NOT…

A diet book. We don't dig diets. Every BODY is different and we don't like people telling us what to feed our bodies. So we will not be doing the same for you.

A weight loss book. We're here to release emotional weight, and if you do need to lose physical weight, you'll notice that usually comes as a byproduct of releasing emotional weight. So, stick around and see what happens. You've truly got nothing to lose!

A quick fix. We believe that small steps lead us to lasting transformational changes. That is how we got where we are. Every day we choose to love our bodies in the moment. Not tomorrow. Not yesterday. Today. Right here and right now. And, most importantly, we really take time to marinate in what's going on with us.

A journey for you to BS. If you're looking to be healed in a week, if you're a chronic procrastinator, if you're lazy, or if you don't want to put in the good ol' elbow grease...this may not be the journey for you. But if you're ready to live a soulful, energizing, enriching life experience, and ready to make that change and put in the work, then you are home, my soul sister. We are so blessed to have you here on this journey with us. Put in the work. DO the journaling exercises with heart and soul and with a deep desire to get to know yourself better. Prepare and eat the recipes. Do your BODYpeace meditation every day. Follow this plan and you will achieve exactly what you need from this journey.

A cookie-cutter plan. Feel free to split up your days. If you want to meditate in the morning and then journal in the evening, go for it. If you want to do it all in the morning, awesome. The only thing we ask is that you commit to doing the BODYpeace meditation every morning upon waking. This is SUPER important. Trust us!

BODYpeace VOCAB

Universe: The Universe is the ever-present energy of love that is within you and around you at all times. Some people call it God, Spirit, Life Force, etc. It doesn't matter what you call it, but we're just going to stick with Universe to keep things uniform. Feel free to replace it with whatever you want. The Universe speaks to you through your inner soul sister.

Inner Soul Sister: Your inner guidance system. Think of it like your own personal GPS system that tells you where to go, what to do, and what to say. You'll feel her guidance and presence in the center of your heart.

Ego: Any fear-based thought or limiting belief is the voice of your ego. A thought that is rooted in fear, anxiety, panic, anger, sadness, shame, or guilt is coming from your ego. Your ego's thoughts are not real. All of your inner soul sister's thoughts are real. All of your inner soul sister's thoughts are love, and all of your ego's thoughts are a call for love.

Soul Scripture: An affirmation that you take with you for the entire day. Consider it your daily BFF. Print it out and keep it in your pocket, make it your desktop icon, or your phone's background. We recommend writing it on a piece of paper and keeping it on your desk to look at for the day, or setting an alarm on your phone to go off every hour to remind you of your Soul Scripture. Share them with everyone you know who needs them. You are officially a BODYpeace messenger!

Miracle: A mental shift in perception from fear to love. Yep, that's it. No fancy skies parting or a dude in a beard coming down to give you a message. A miracle is when you choose to change your mind about something - when you choose to stop your fearful thoughts in their tracks and think loving thoughts instead. Miracles are the result of *correct thinking*, meaning they align your perceptions with love and bring you a sense of peace.

Fuel: Food. Just like your car needs fuel to make its engine work, you need food to make your body work.

What to Expect on the
BODYpeace Journey

For the first fifteen days of your journey, Heather will be guiding you through fifteen BODYtruths. The BODYtruth portion of your journey is all about learning to develop a soul sister's mindset. You see, your problem is not your body. Your problem is the thoughts you have about your body. As you start to reframe your mind about your body and food, you free yourself from the BODYlies you've been telling yourself and awaken to your BODYtruths. Consider this fifteen days of pure awakening, baby!

Each day centers around one BODYtruth. You'll begin each day with your soothing BODYpeace meditation to get you into the BODYpeace state of mind. You'll follow your meditation with reading your BODYtruth section and doing your journaling exercises for the day. These tools are the exact ones Heather has used to achieve BODYfreedom. If you follow each day, by the end of the fifteen days, you will feel a big shift in the way you see yourself, your body, and your world!

For the final fifteen days of your journey, Kasey will be guiding you through fifteen BODYfuel recipes and exercises. Kasey will help you take the fear out of food and turn it into fuel for your body. Each topic will be accompanied by a story or words of encouragement as to how you may face a similar struggle but can overcome it in your own way. You will begin breaking the mold of using fitness and food as a way to restrict yourself. In turn, you'll learn to embrace them as a way to fuel your new sense of strength.

BODYpeace Checklist

Before you begin your journey, it's important to make sure you have all the tools necessary to make sure your experience is the best it can be.

We have included many elements in addition to the physical book. There are meditations, exercise videos, bonus recipes, and an amazing online community to help support you on your journey.

Here is our simple checklist to make sure you get everything you can out of this journey:

❑ Check out http://bodypeacemovement.com/book where all of your meditations, tapping videos, and workouts are located, and join our online community!

❑ Get a specially designated BODYpeace journal to use during your journey.

❑ Set the time and energy aside for this amazing ride!

❑ Set Your BODYpeace Intention.

When we chatted about having you set a BODYpeace intention, we instantly got butterflies. This, dear reader, is where the magic happens. You are so powerful, and your intentions are the root of all your power. When you set an intention before beginning a journey like this, you give yourself clarity and a sense of purpose as you move along.

NOTE: Don't BS yourself. Be 100% honest with yourself. The more honest you are, the more successful you will be.

1.) What does your relationship with your body feel like? When you look in the mirror, what thoughts run through your mind?

_____

_____

_____

_____

_____

_____

_____

_____

_____

_____

_____

_____

_____

_____

_____

_____

2.) What does your relationship with food feel like? When you think of eating a meal, what thoughts run through your mind?

_____

_____

_____

_____

_____

_____

_____

_____

_____

_____

_____

_____

_____

3.) How do you want to feel at the end of your BODYpeace journey? Take your time with this one. Close your eyes. What do you see? What do you look like? How do you feel? (Hint: A great question to ask yourself is, "What changes would I need to make for a BODYmiracle to occur?" Keep in mind our definition of miracle - shifting your perception from fear to love.)

_____

_____

_____

_____

_____

_____

_____

_____

_____

_____

_____

_____

_____

_____

_____

_____

4.) Re-read your answer to question three. As you read through your response, what three feelings light you up inside? Those words are your BODYpeace intention!

_____

_____

_____

_____

_____

_____

_____

_____

_____

_____

_____

_____

_____

We know what you're thinking: "How can just three words sum up my BODYpeace intention?" We do what we do because we want to feel a certain way. And we want what we want because we want to feel a certain way. These three words sum up why you chose to take your

BODYpeace journey, and they sum up how you want to feel at the end of your BODYpeace journey. Now, let's make your BODYpeace intention your reality!

Your BODYtruths - Discovering the Real You

Hi dear reader, it's Heather here. And this is officially the beginning of your BODYpeace journey! As I embarked upon my BODYpeace journey, I renamed my ~~recovery~~ journey a discovery journey. Once I understood that I didn't need to change my body, but I did need to change my thoughts about my body, I realized I wasn't really recovering from anything - I was discovering who I really was. That is what your BODYtruth phase is all about. This is your rite of passage to discovering the real you. Every word and every exercise is backed with a whole lot of soul and is designed to help you expand your awareness of your body and your relationship with food. When that happens, you transform.

For the first half of BODYtruth, you're going to reframe your perception of your body. Then for the second half, you're going to transform your perception of food. These are all of the goods I used to turn my BODYlies into BODYtruths so that I could live the BODYpeace lifestyle I live today.

To kick off every day, you're going to settle in with your BODYpeace meditation. (All the meditations and more can be found at http://bodypeacemovement.com/book) This meditation will take you out of a state of BODYshame and into a state of BODYpeace. We suggest that you do it every day for the next fifteen days. If you want to keep doing it after that, go for it! The BODYpeace meditation is incredibly powerful. It's the perfect daily warm-up to your BODYtruth exercises. It will tune you in, pump you up, and help you open your mind to receive all the guidance you're going to receive during the next fifteen days.

Before you start the meditation, call to mind your BODYpeace intention. Hold that intention close to your heart and then start your BODYpeace meditation! When you declare an intention and infuse it into a spiritual practice like meditation, incredible miracles go down for you! After you set your intention, all you have to do is sit back, relax, and let my voice be your guide.

Make sure you rely on your soul sisters in the BODYpeace Facebook community who are doing all of this right alongside you. You are never alone and have so much support on your side. May you have a blessed and soulful journey. We'll be holding your hand every step of the way.

How I Found My BODYtruths

I didn't find spirituality. Spirituality found me. It found me while I was drifting off into space in an empty church pew. And it found me again when I was rolled up in a ball, crying myself to sleep on the basement floor.

Growing up, I was your typical "good girl." I believed that in order to feel good enough, I had to "be good" and "do good" in the eyes of my parents and in the eyes of my religion. I was raised in a multi-faith household - my father was Jewish and my mother was Catholic. But I was raised Catholic. My dad went to mass with us every week and, when I was seven years old, he decided to convert to Catholicism.

The day he decided to convert, a really amazing miracle happened to him. He was going out for his daily summer run. There was a huge hill near our house, and he always had a hell of a time going up it. When he reached the hill and started running up it, he didn't experience the resistance and weight in his quads like he was used to. He didn't have to talk himself into running up it at a steady pace. He didn't have to manage his breath. My dad said that he felt like he was floating up the hill and all he could see was white light blinding him. He wasn't afraid; he felt safe, loved, and infinite. In that moment, he heard a voice tell him, "It's time to convert. You're ready."

I'll never forget that story of how the Universe came to my father. It was my first time being a witness to a spiritual experience. I remember being amazed and in shock, seeing my mom and dad hugging and crying. I felt so connected, peaceful, amazed, and filled with light. I felt infinite.

Bearing witness to that incredible experience, I

continued to play the "good girl" card. I lived my life for my parents and for my religion. I was raised to "honor thy father and mother." But, I didn't get the memo of what the word *honor* really meant. Instead, I idolized my parents. I put them on a pedestal and, for the most part, did what they told me to do. I rarely fought back with them because I just thought they were always right about everything. I thought my parents knew best and I thought they knew better than me. I wasn't really encouraged to think for myself.

Up until I was a young adult, I never questioned my religion. I was taught that Catholicism held all of the answers to my questions. I was taught to pray and I did it…but I didn't really understand what prayer meant. Whenever I asked someone to explain it to me, the explanation never satisfied me. The explanation felt complicated and empty, and I wound up feeling confused and disconnected from God. I had faith - I knew there was a power greater than me guiding me through everything - but I didn't feel that deep connection I desired. And I was afraid to admit to myself that I wasn't going to find that deep connection in Catholicism.

Fast forwarding to my senior year of high school, I experienced a spiritual awakening. Things weren't going well at home. My mom was chronically drinking, and her alcoholism was getting worse by the day. My parents were arguing all the time. I felt so lonely because I had no siblings. I felt that no one could relate to the hell that was erupting in my household - and in my heart. As my parents' relationship was being torn apart, so was I.

One Sunday morning, I went to church by myself. As my parents' relationship became rockier, I started to distance myself from them. It was so painful to see my mom destroying herself with alcohol, and it was even more painful watching my parents fake their relationship. For them, church became this alternate reality they could escape to for an hour and pretend that everything was like it used to be. As I walked into church solo, I decided to sit in the back of the church. As the priest was giving his sermon, I felt this rush of energy flood through my body and stop at my heart. It was unlike anything I'd ever experienced before. It was like God was talking directly to me. It felt warm, light, and peaceful. My hands were tingling and my heart felt like a flame that had just been ignited. In that moment, I realized that I didn't need to go to church in order to experience God like I had been taught growing up. I realized that Spirit would still speak to me regardless if I showed up for a weekly sermon or not. In that moment, I felt more connected to God than I ever had in my life. I felt infinite. I knew this feeling…it was the same feeling I'd felt when my dad had his out-of-body experience running. That's when it hit me - God wasn't found in a church. God was found in an experience.

I felt so free, connected, and joyful. I wanted to shout it from the rooftops!

…And then, I felt scared.

At that moment, I knew there was a deeper connection

that I was seeking, and I knew I was on track to reconnecting with it. But I also knew I wasn't going to reconnect with it at church every week. It just wasn't my truth. Instantly, my ego spiraled out of control and all I could think about was what my parents and my community would think. Would they be mad at me? Would they be ashamed of me? Would they judge me?

I chose to follow my fear that day. I decided to continue going to church. I felt like the last thing my parents needed was another disappointment. So, in typical Heather fashion, I starved my truth to feed the truths of others. Also in typical Heather fashion, I literally starved myself. I felt so out of control. I felt trapped. I felt like I couldn't speak my truth or voice my needs, so I controlled what I knew I could control - food and exercise. Every time I starved my truth, I starved myself more and my eating disorder got progressively worse. I was subsiding on 900 – 1200 calories per day and 60 minutes of cardio every day. I didn't realize this was what I was doing at the time. In my mind, the thinner I could become, the happier I would become. I thought that being thinner would somehow make up for the emptiness I felt from being a bonafide people-pleaser.

Three years later, Spirit had another go 'round. I was in my third year of college, and nothing had changed at home. Actually, it had gotten worse. My mom was majorly depressed, drunk all the time, and yo-yoed between frightening outbursts and passing out on the bed. My dad was always looking for ways to escape being at home. He felt hopeless about my mom and their marriage. I came home from college every weekend to work and I stayed at my parents' home. I didn't have to do that, but I chose to. I think I felt that by being at home I could soften the blow and create more peace. I walked on eggshells around everyone. I could feel the toxic energy, and the violent outbursts and manipulative behavior from my mom which became almost too much to handle. I knew it wasn't the real her. I knew she had a disease. I wanted to help her, but I couldn't. Again, I felt trapped. I felt like a prisoner in my own home. I felt so broken.

By this time, I was restricting my food during the day, binging at night, and purging with exercise. It was a nasty cycle. I would restrict myself to only "healthy" foods during the day and would eat them at specific times instead of listening to my body's hunger cues. I didn't understand that my body needed food for vitality and that it also needed food for pleasure. Because of the restriction during the day, I would then binge at night because that's when shit got real. It was easy to distract myself during the day from the pain and suffering I was experiencing with my home life. But at night, it was harder to do that. And that is exactly when I was faced with my emotions. I didn't know how to cope with it in a healthy way, so I coped with it in the only way that I knew how to at the time: by numbing myself out with food.

One summer night, I went to Bikram yoga with my friend

Jenn. After yoga, we sat in the parking lot and ate some dinner we'd packed. It was a warm, gentle summer night. I'd just started reading Spirit Junkie by Gabrielle Bernstein and I was so moved by it. Every word hit my soul and made me feel free. It made me feel like the God I had always prayed to was not the God I thought I knew, and I loved that. With every page I turned, I found myself feeling that same experience I felt that day in the back of church.

When I got home from yoga, a huge wave of dread washed over me. I didn't want to go in my house. I was afraid of what mess I was going to walk into. It wasn't home. It was hell. Feeling out of control, I walked over to the snack cabinet in my kitchen and reached for a huge bag of sea salt popcorn that I was more than ready to binge on. "NO!" I screamed and slammed the door shut. I ran downstairs, hit my knees, and had my moment of spiritual surrender. "I can't do this anymore. I don't even know what you are. I don't even know if I believe in you. But, I need help. Please help me." I fell into a ball and sobbed endlessly for what seemed like hours. Eventually, I peeled myself off the floor and walked upstairs to bed.

The next morning, I woke up and heard my inner soul sister say to me, "I am here. I've always been here. But now it's time to learn the truth about me. You know where to go and you know what to do." I did know. I knew exactly what to do. I hopped on the computer and clicked the purchase button, and that was it. *A Course in Miracles* would arrive on my doorstep in seven days.

After starting to read A Course in Miracles, I started to see everything in my life differently. And in that process, things started to fall apart. My mom's drinking got worse and her behavior was beyond scary and out of control. I lived in fear of what she would do next and what episode I would arrive home to.

My parents got divorced and I moved in with a friend while my dad lived in a trailer and figured out his next move. Meanwhile, I hated my job, my relationship was on the rocks, and I even hated my blog.

At the time, I'd been blogging as a healthy living blogger, focusing on food and fitness and chronicling my everyday eats and workouts. It had become increasingly clear to me that this was all a cover-up. My blog was a façade that kept me stuck in the cycle of my eating disorder, furthering my obsession with food and fitness, and reiterating my unwillingness to just be myself. I was afraid of sharing who I was because I was afraid of being rejected. It kept me in the spiritual closet. But I was ready to come out now. I was ready to share what I was learning and I was ready to let my light shine and be my true self.

So, I did. And it felt awesome.

When I told my parents that I was leaving church for a meditation pillow, a homemade altar, and a 700+ page text called A Course in Miracles, they were not exactly thrilled. They thought I was doing this as a way to rebel against them and against the church. Sure, it might have looked that way, but that wasn't the truth. Their divorce - their breakup - broke me open. It broke me wide open and freed me from the years I'd spent living under their truths instead of living my own. I have nothing but gratitude for it. Their divorce awakened me on a deep, deep level. It awakened me to a whole new world and to the real me. Of course, wounds were fresh and it didn't feel right telling them that whole spiel at the time. But I didn't have to tell them because, for once, I felt so secure and strong in my own choices. I felt defenseless, and that felt so freeing.

I was tested for months and months after that. My dad went through waves of pretending to be okay with me not going to church with him. Then he'd be really angry that I wasn't going to church with him. I received letters from my old priest who told me I was being an unloving daughter and urged me to come back to the church. I received post cards from my nana who said that I was being a horrible daughter by not going to church and that I needed to be forgiven by God.

Every time, my ego would flare up and tell me I was being a bad daughter and that I was being unloving. But when I sat and got still, I would hear my inner soul sister tell me the opposite: "Keep speaking your truth firmly and with love." I would hear it - just like clockwork. Every time. Those same eight words. So, I did. Even though it was so hard for me, I kept speaking my truth and standing my ground. We teach people how to treat us, and I was un-teaching these people about who I really was. No more "sweet Heather" who always does what's expected of her. It was time for the real me to emerge - independent, strong, and confident in my beliefs.

I am proud of the woman I have become, and I am proud of the perseverance I've shown through it all. We all have our own hurdles to jump and mine have not been an easy feat. It's been one big coming out journey and really, my dear reader, you have been the inspiration all along. If we don't have a mentality of service behind what we're doing, then I don't think we can survive our darkest hours. Even when I was binging and purging, even when I was crying myself to sleep at night for fear of my mom having another violent episode, even when I was sleeping in my friend's spare room wondering how I was going to make enough money to support myself, I had a nano-ounce of faith. Sure, there were plenty of times when I would think, "Really? This is happening right now?" But, thanks to the Course, I knew how to take myself out of victim mode and into student mode. I knew, as the Course says, "There is no problem in any situation that faith will not solve." I intuitively sensed and knew that if I could learn my lessons from my parents and from my eating disorder, I would be free and then I could teach those lessons to others.

So, what did I learn?

I learned that people are just people like me. We are all

doing the best we can with the knowledge we have.

I learned that I can speak my truth firmly and with love. Both can be sent and received at the same time.

I learned that no one outside of me holds the answer to what is true for me. Not my parents, not a mentor, not a friend, not my boyfriend. Only I do. I learned that I don't have to look outside for what I already have inside.

I learned that my sensitivity is a profound gift because when you can feel what people feel, you know how to help them heal.

I learned that relationships and addictions are beautiful assignments for my soul's growth and healing.

I learned that shitty moments are shiny moments in disguise, propelling you toward your light and urging you to own your greatness.

I learned that only what I am not giving can be lacking in any situation. I have to give what I want to receive.

But most importantly, I learned that in order to figure out what I wanted, I needed to break away from what I'd known. I needed to break away from what was keeping me stuck in a false sense of safety, and I needed a blank canvas to paint whatever I wanted on it.

This is the gift that Spirituality has given me. With religion, I was told where to go, what to do, and what to say. I was told that something outside of me had the answers, and I had to keep seeking it until I found peace. With Spirituality, I am told to first ask where to go, what to do, and what to say.

And then, I am told to wait - to wait with patience and trust that everything I need is given to me and will flow through me in perfect timing. I am told that nothing outside of me has the answers, but everything inside of me does, and that is how I know true peace.

You are always being given opportunities to heal but, you have a choice - you can either break down or, as Elizabeth Lesser says, you can allow the Universe to break you open.

The road you travel will always have twists and turns, but it is paved perfectly for you. If you are willing to build your faith muscle by marinating in the mystery of the assignments that are laid before you, you will learn peace. Fear might be there, but it will not have a hold on you because you will trust that the Universe, and your invisible team of angels, are holding your hand and guiding you through the storm.

I choose to embrace life as a journey. Every person, situation, and relationship I encounter is a stop along the way, given to me as an opportunity to extend and receive love. And because of this, I've come to see my body as that - a beautiful vessel through which I give and receive love. Every day is a new opportunity to remove BODYlies from my life and welcome BODYtruths into it. I continue to awaken to my own BODYtruths and remove myself from anyone else's perception of what healthy and beautiful are. Only I can define that for me. And only you can define that for you.

BODYtruths

The Meaning Behind It All: What Are BODYtruths?

How did you treat your body as a baby? Think back to the earliest memory you have of being a baby. How did you react to your body? We can learn so much from our little selves.

Up until age two, being naked was my jam. I was a free bird and a ridiculously happy baby. I would flaunt my goodies and freely dance around the house without a care in the world. I loved being naked and I loved being in my body, and there was almost always a song flying out of my mouth. I was so comfortable in my body because I was so sure of its purpose. I didn't dissect my body or pinch the extra fat on my little legs and arms. I was fascinated by my legs' ability to carry me from place to place, and I was in awe of my hands' ability able to pick up this wondrous thing called food and place it into my mouth. The simple things that my body could do fascinated me. What was most important to me though, was using my body as a vehicle through which I could be free and happy. Those were my BODYtruths.

Somewhere along the way, I ditched that message, and the seemingly simple things that my body could do for me became…well…boring. They wore out their welcome and were replaced by my fascination with Disney princesses. Those damn fairy tales get us every time, don't they? I would wake my mom up at 5:00 a.m. sporting a tutu and my favorite Cinderella sweatshirt, so excited and ready to go. My mom would wipe the crusties from her eyes and follow me into the den where I would put on that day's performance for her. Beauty and the Beast, Snow White, Cinderella, Aladdin… you name it and I performed it! I would reenact every scene with so much grit and grace but I can remember, even at that young age, wanting so badly to be a princess too. I loved performing but, what I wanted more than anything, was to be them. They were so beautiful to me and they were the epitome of happiness. I idolized them. I bought into this BODYlie that, in order to be truly happy, I had to look like them, talk like them, sing like them, and find my own "perfect" prince charming.

As I got older, my fascination with Disney princesses

dwindled, but my obsession with idolizing girls who were older than me continued. It was an endless cycle. I was always looking to older girls to emulate and idolize, thinking that if I could have their bodies, be as popular as them, and receive all those mysterious glances from cute boys, that I would finally be happy. I fed into these false expectations and ideals - these BODYlies - and it continued for years.

It wasn't until nearly twenty years later that I realized I had to stop reaching for those BODYlies and start to develop my own BODYtruths. And now you have fifteen of them, which I've laid out for you in the first half of your BODYpeace journey. For the next fifteen days, you are going to explore your own BODYtruths. You are going to learn the purpose of your body and the purpose of food as it applies to your soulful, gorgeous being. You are going to be armed with spiritual tools that you can take with you for the rest of your life.

BODYtruths are thoughts you choose to believe about your body that make you feel free in your body, safe in your skin, and connected to your spirit. And that is what the next fifteen days are all about. We are going to equip you with the spiritual tools (BODYtruths) that will help you maintain a sense of BODYpeace and prime you for the second half of your BODYpeace journey.

DAY 1
OWN IT

Hey there, gorgeous!

We are starting with something that you're probably not used to doing - feeling your shit. We can sometimes work so hard to avoid owning up to our emotions. We paint this big, scary picture of these feelings, like monsters in the back of our mind's closet, and then we get fearful. That fear manifests as anxiety and that's when we think that looking inside ourselves is too scary, so we search outside of ourselves for answers. We try to find love in food, we try to find love in exercise, or we try to numb out those feelings with over-eating, binging, or restricting. We use food and fitness to cover up the wound, convincing ourselves that it will just go away. But it doesn't go away.

Nothing ever goes away until it teaches us what we need to learn. So, you're not wrong for having a food addiction or having a really shitty relationship with your body. You just haven't yet learned the lesson it's trying to teach you. But that's what your BODYpeace journey is for - to help you learn the lessons you need to learn.

The first step to achieving BODYpeace is simply accepting that you have an unhealthy relationship with your body. This is so powerful because you are giving yourself the opportunity to feel exactly how you need to feel. Not how you think you should feel, not what you think your parents would want you to feel, not what you think is the most "spiritual" way to feel, but exactly how you need to feel. And that boils down to you being present for yourself, showing up for yourself, and being willing to have the courage to be here. I know you want to have BODYpeace now, but the reason that you haven't reached that space yet is because you're so focused on getting "there" and not focused enough on being here. And here is the best place to start. It's the most honest place to start, and from honesty comes clarity and true healing.

One of the BODYlies you've been telling yourself is that you're not good enough exactly as you are. You want to flip that BODYlie into a BODYtruth, and the way you do that is by getting into the practice of accepting yourself without judgment.

Have you accepted that you are in a state of BODYchaos? Before you can make any real and lasting change, you have to accept where you are in your BODYpeace journey. It sounds counterintuitive, huh? Think of it this way - you can't self-hate yourself into self-acceptance. You have to meet yourself where you are and then co-create an action plan with the Universe to move forward. You already have your action plan (Hello, BODYpeace!) so all you have to do is follow it and you will move forward. Without acceptance, you stay stuck.

Accepting where you are - right here and right now - is the beginning of a whole new relationship with yourself. I know what you're thinking: "How can I accept where I am and still love myself when I don't know how?" The good news is that you don't have to know how to change - you just have to be willing to change.

Acceptance is not giving up. Acceptance is giving in to the Universe's plan for you, which is always so much greater than anything you could conceive with your silly little mind. Acceptance lets you off the hook and gives you freedom.

In my first coaching session with one of my clients, I could tell that she needed this breakthrough to happen. She needed to be willing to accept exactly where she was in her BODYpeace journey - right there in that coaching session with me - as a divine step in her own discovery journey.

"Are you willing to accept yourself?" I asked her.

She stammered, "Um...um...yes."

"Okay, then say it out loud, girl," I told her.

"I accept myself. I accept where I am in my BODYpeace journey," she said.

"Keep going," I urged. And she did. She kept saying it over and over and, the more she said it, the more her eyes filled up with tears.

She kept saying it for two minutes straight. And then she said, "Wow. I feel so free...I didn't know how powerful that would be until I actually did it."

When you accept yourself, you are accepting your soul. When you accept yourself, you let yourself off the hook and give yourself an opportunity to create a new reality of inner peace, happiness, and freedom.

This was totally the case for me. I had to first accept that I had an unhealthy relationship with my body in order to create a new, healthier relationship with my body. My ego didn't want me to do that because it wanted me to stay stuck in fear and BODYchaos. I felt so much resistance to the idea of accepting myself because it felt like I was admitting defeat. When I decided to make that step, I felt this weight lift off of me. It was like I'd been carrying a backpack full of self-hate for miles up a mountain and someone just took it off my back. Even though I knew I had a long journey ahead of me, for the first time in eight years, I felt real hope that I could create a life of BODYpeace.

Without a desire to learn self-acceptance, I wouldn't be where I am today. And neither would you - because there has to be some part of you that wants to accept yourself if you wound up reading this book.

Kris Carr said something on an episode of Super Soul Sunday that hit me hard (in the good way). She said something to the effect of: Would you scream at a patch of dry grass because it's not lush and green? No. First, you meet the grass where it is. You accept that it's all dried up and then you give the grass some TLC to nurture it into better and greener days. The grass couldn't get better until you accepted that it was dried up. Once you accepted it was weak, you could open up your mind to receive guidance to heal it. The same goes for you, sweet friend. When you embrace acceptance, that's when your healing really begins. Honor yourself for where you are now and commit to becoming your own healer. We will be your wings until you can fly on your own. We will guide you every step of the way. For now, start to open up to holding your own hand as you walk along your BODYpeace journey.

Channel Your Inner Soul Sister

Your BODYpeace meditation is going to become your new BFF for the next thirty days (Remember, you can practice them all at http://bodypeacemovement.com/book). Every day, you're going to sit your pretty butt down and tune into the rhythm of your inner soul sister. Listen to your BODYpeace Meditation today and let yourself be reminded of the true purpose of your body. Before you sit down and close your eyes, set your intention as you listen to the soft whispers of your heart. Feel the spirit of acceptance flow through your body.

I know the idea of accepting yourself feels counterintuitive. "How can I accept myself if I don't know how?" is probably running through your mind. Just trust the process and go with it.

Grab your BODYpeace journal and channel your inner soul sister with a free write. There is no wrong way to free write because it's coming straight from your heart. Just let the pen flow across the page. If you feel resistance, good! We always resist the things we need the most. Go ahead and answer these questions in your BODYpeace journal:

- Where are you right now on your journey to BODYpeace? How do you feel about your body? What is your story that led you to this moment?

- Are you willing to accept yourself? (This is the most important part. "Willing" is the magic word. All you need is to be willing to change. Your willingness is everything. The Universe will take care of the rest.)

- How do you want to feel at the end of this journey? How do you most want to feel in your body?

- What does it feel like to hate yourself?

Any level of stress or discomfort means you are believing an untrue thought. Let's flip that switch, shall we?

- What does it feel like to accept yourself?

- What is one thing you can do today to show

yourself love in the form of self-acceptance? Commit to doing this every day for the duration of your BODYpeace journey. Hold yourself accountable by posting it for everyone in the BODYpeace Facebook community! We want to support you.

SOUL SCRIPTURE

When I embrace self-acceptance, my healing can begin. #BODYpeace

DAY 2
IT'S SPIRITUALLY HEALTHY TO BE SAD

Can I ask you a question? When you're sad, angry, or upset, do you feel like you're wrong for feeling that way? Do you feel wrong for feeling sad? In my experience with coaching soul sisters, just like you, I came to find they all shared this one crazy belief. There was this underlying sense that being positive and being happy were the same thing, and that you couldn't be a positive person and feel sad, angry, or upset at the same time. Let's bust that myth right now. There is a reason we are spiritual beings having a human experience. Human emotions are a natural part of your human existence. As human beings, we have a rainbow of emotions. Many of those human emotions are sadness, despair, anger, frustration, guilt, and shame. You can still be positive and feel those feelings. It's kind of insane to think that, in order to live a positive and happy life, we can't have tough times. It is spiritually healthy to be sad! Marianne Williamson says it best: "Even a happy life has sad days."

When you're sad, it simply means an unhealed aspect of you wants to be healed. Any sort of sadness or discomfort you feel is your body's way of saying to you, "Help me set myself free." Your job is to treat yourself with compassion and allow that unhealed aspect of yourself to come up so it can get out. This is probably where you often get stuck. An uncomfortable feeling comes up and you think, "Ah! I can't handle this. It's too painful," or, "There's something wrong with me for feeling this way! Ugh, I just want it to go away." At this point, you reach for the bag of popcorn or the pint of ice cream. Instead of thinking of these feelings as signs that you're doing something wrong, think of them as signs from your inner soul sister that it's time to get to work.

Your BODYpeace healing process is a detox; your emotions have to come up in order for them to be healed. They have to come up through your body in order to get out of your body. So, when you're sad, you're not doing something wrong - you're just detoxing. It's your inner soul sister's way of signaling to you that you're ready to shed a layer of fear that you don't need anymore.

I understand how painful it is to say to yourself, "Ugh, I can't believe I just did that." I also understand how painful it is to say to yourself, "Ugh, I can't believe I did that again." Whatever your "again" is - whether it's overeating, under-eating, over-exercising, binge drinking, losing your shit on your partner, or sending that really snarky text - you start to realize it's much deeper than just an unhealthy behavior. It's an unhealthy habit that you've created.

In the early stages of my ~~recovery~~ discovery from anorexia and overeating, I thought I was doing something wrong when I started to take a spiritually-based approach to healing because I kept overeating at night. I kept restricting my calories the next day, and I kept over-exercising to make up for it all. I thought that following this spiritual blueprint of meditating, journaling, and feeling my feelings would fully heal everything instantly. I was looking for another shortcut. Sound familiar?

There is a reason we're calling this a BODYpeace journey. Because it's just that - a journey. You're here to marinate in all the stuff you used to numb out. You're here to marinate in the mystery of those feelings that don't feel so hot. Why? Because there is an amazing lesson beneath each one of those just waiting to reveal itself to you. And once you learn that lesson, you are meant to teach it to others. We teach what we need to learn.

Here's the deal, gorgeous - you can't measure the success of your healing process based on whether you're still engaging in your behavior or not. Why? Because it becomes a habit, and habits take time to break. What's more important, if you're still engaging in unhealthy patterns, is that you know it's a habit and you're ready to change it. That's phase one - just admitting that you're ready to change. So, are you ready to change? Are you ready to let go of that habit? I think you are because you ended up right here.

Channel Your Inner Soul Sister

Be patient with yourself and have compassion for the unhealed parts of yourself. Patience and compassion are key ingredients to living the BODYpeace life. Remember that the unhealed parts of you are not bad. They just need some TLC from you so they can be healed. *A Course in Miracles* says, "You cannot bring the light to the darkness. You have to bring the darkness to the light." Soul sister translation: Take the unhealed parts of yourself and ask the Universe to help you heal them.

That's all you have to do. It really is that simple...we just tend to overcomplicate things because we want the results right now. But your BODYpeace journey is just that - a journey. Celebrate that. If you're feeling sad, marinate in that sadness for a bit. If you're feeling angry, marinate in that anger for a bit. If you're feeling anxious, marinate in that anxiety. And by marinate in it, I mean accept it. I used to be so self-conscious of my body that waiting in line at the local coffee shop was painful. I would stand there with my arms crossed and stare down at the ground, hoping that no one would pay attention to me. I noticed this one day and I just made it a practice to marinate in the discomfort I felt. I would take deep breaths in line and mentally tell myself, "I accept that I am self-conscious of my body as I wait here in line. I am willing to feel this unhealed part of me. Show me how to heal it." Almost instantly, I felt the discomfort start to dissipate from my body and that jump-started that part of me that needed to heal.

Grab your BODYpeace journal. We become sad because there is an unhealed aspect of ourselves wanting to be healed. Any hang-ups you have about your body image that make you hate yourself are unhealed aspects of yourself that want to be healed. And often times, that sadness stems from unrealistic expectations that we hold for ourselves. When we, or other people, don't live up to those expectations, we become sad and go through a grieving process. But you're not grieving yourself or a person - you're grieving the expectation you've placed upon them. That expectation not being met is what tore you to shreds.

We are taught that we need to look outside ourselves for love and happiness. We are taught that once we have that love and happiness we've been searching for, whether it's in a romantic partner, in your family, in your career, or in food, we have to hold onto it tightly and not let it slip away. If we let it slip away, then love slips away and we feel incomplete.

But here's the deal - as long as you are looking to something outside of yourself to fill you up, you will always feel empty. No one can take the place of the love you've been seeking. Only you can do that. No one can ever give you the love you've been searching for because that love lives within you.

So, now it's your turn. Take a deep breath in and out through your nose and center yourself into this exercise with this prayer: "Dear Universe, please guide me to be gentle and honest with myself so I can heal and transform the unhealed parts of me. Thank you."

Now, answer these questions in your BODYpeace journal:

What are my expectations about love? List out every single one.

How have my expectations of love been shattered?

How are these shattered expectations linked to my disordered eating and/or disordered exercise compulsions? Take your time with this one. If you need extra guidance, repeat the above prayer.

Now that you've let it all out, it's time to let it all go. Let's get into the practice of releasing your ego-based feelings to the Universe. A Course in Miracles says, "I cannot take from you what you will not release to me." You don't need to know how to release your ego-based feelings. You just need to be willing to release those feelings to the Universe and let your inner soul sister re-interpret them for you.

Take a deep breath and write this down in your notebook below all of the work you just did: "I am willing to release all of these expectations I've projected onto myself and others. I know they are not serving me and I am ready to let them go. Universe, show me how."

Amazing work today, sister. I know this stuff isn't a total picnic, but the clarity that comes after it totally is. I suggest going back through this exercise and reading what you wrote. Often times, your inner soul sister will pipe up with even more wisdom to pour through you and help you reach a different height of epiphany.

SOUL SCRIPTURE

With every breakdown comes a breakthrough.

#BODYpeace

DAY 3
YOUR ~~RECOVERY~~ DISCOVERY JOURNEY

You are never alone, my sweet friend. I repeat - you are never ever alone. As you walk down this BODYpeace journey, you not only have us and the entire BODYpeace community holding you up but, most importantly, you always have your own inner support system with your number one gal pal - your inner soul sister.

One of my all-time favorite lessons from *A Course in Miracles* is, "If you knew who walks beside you on this path that you have chosen, fear would be impossible." When you think you are alone, your ego wants to convince you that, because no one is physically sitting next to you, you are alone and should feel lonely. But there is so much invisible help within you and around you. For starters, you have the ever-present guidance and love coming from the Universe through your inner soul sister. The Universe speaks to you through her. Beyond that, you have invisible guides in the form of angels, deceased loved ones, and ascended masters (also known as spiritually enlightened teachers) like Jesus, Buddha, Gandhi, etc. If those are just words to you or they don't resonate with you, that's totally fine. Take what you need and leave the rest. But if you want to connect with these invisible beings, just ask them to guide you. They're waiting for your call!

You have a full-time BFF in your inner soul sister. Call on

her whenever you need to. She is always waiting to give you clear guidance and direction on where to go, what to do, and what to say.

Not only are you not alone, but you can't make this journey alone. Without a spiritual connection, you are powerless. The Universe is the battery and your body is the engine. You can't go without the power of the Universe moving through you. If you could have done this alone, you would have achieved BODYpeace by now.

I remember the first time I hit my knees - I mean really hit my knees - and admitted that I was powerless over my addiction to food and exercise. I thought it was going to be scary because I was afraid of losing that false sense of control that I was getting from my eating disorder. Although tears flowed endlessly down my cheeks, they were tears of clarity. With each drop that made its way down my face, I felt like I was shedding false layers of myself and making room for new ones to pile up. I felt free and connected to an energy greater than myself and that experience of feeling the Universe's presence with me changed me in a deep way. From that moment on, I made it my mission to commit to plugging into that power source every day. And that made me feel limitless and powerful. When I admitted that I was powerless, I actually gained power. In that moment of admitting defeat to the body image war circling through my brain, I invited the Universe to show me how to create a loving relationship with my inner soul sister.

Are you willing to admit that you are powerless? Are you willing to surrender your addictive patterns?

Surrender isn't giving up - it's giving IN to the Universe's plan for you, which is far better than anything you could conceive with your mind.

It's time to shine an honest and compassionate light on yourself. When you're in that addictive pattern - I mean really in it, like fistful in a bag of chocolates, or mid-binge, or killing yourself on the treadmill to burn off your last meal - you alone don't have the mental capacity to get yourself out of that addictive behavior pattern. That's why you need a spiritual intervention. And that's why you need to ask the Universe for help - because you can't do it alone. You need to invite your inner soul sister to guide you and hold your hand on your BODYpeace journey. It's time to become your own best friend.

"But, how?" you ask.

This is about the time you ask for a miracle.

Remember that the miracle begins with you choosing to see things from a loving perspective instead of a fearful perspective. The moment you feel yourself make that mental shift from fear to love is when the miracle happens. It's the moment when you are mid-binge and say, "You know what? This isn't serving me. I feel miserable. I'm going to put down this bag of *insert food drug of choice*." It's the moment when you get off the treadmill, your body completely depleted of energy, and say, "Inner soul sister,

I am caught in this addictive cycle and I feel powerless. I need a miracle. Help me stop running from fear and help me run toward love."

What addictive BODYshame pattern are you in? And what miracle do you need to ask for?

Remember that lesson from *A Course in Miracles*? "You cannot bring the light to the darkness. You must bring the darkness to the light." In this case, the darkness is all of your limiting beliefs about your body, and the light is the truth about your body. The darkness is, "I'll only be able to succeed when I'm skinny," or, "When I fit into a size 4, then I'll be happy." The light is, "The only things I need to change about my body are the thoughts I have about my body," or, "My body is not a punching bag to abuse. It is a gorgeous vessel through which I express love."

When you look at the darkness (your addictive behavior) and bring it to the light (your inner soul sister) you set the miracle in motion. That's all you need to do. Your part is recognizing the parts that aren't working for you and honoring your desire to change. That gives the Universe the green light to communicate to you through your inner soul sister and help you change your mind about your situation. It will happen in divine timing - not on your timing. That means you may experience the miracle in five minutes or five days. Sometimes, you have to learn to exercise your faith and patience muscles before the miracle actually happens. Try not to get hung up on that, though. It's most important to stay present in whatever you are feeling. The more present you are in the moment and the more open you are to receive that guidance, the less concerned you'll be about when it will actually happen.

Trust the process and know that all of this is happening for you - not to you. So often, we make ourselves the victim of situations. But the only thing we hold ourselves victim to are our own limiting beliefs. When you're in a victim mentality, you think that you're alone, you think that you're never going to find BODYpeace, and you think that you're going to be stuck in this BODYshame cycle forever. You believe there is no way out and you give in to every thought your ego feeds you. When you're in a soul sister mentality, you trust that the Universe never gives you anything you can't handle. You trust that every single situation that presents itself to you on your BODYpeace journey is a divine opportunity for you to learn BODYpeace. All of your obstacles are opportunities in disguise, urging you to let yourself grow.

Within this BODYshame spiral that you're caught in is a key that unlocks a door to your purpose. A Course in Miracles says, "...what you teach you strengthen in yourself because you are sharing it. Every lesson you teach you are learning." That's why I am here writing this to you. I am teaching BODYpeace to you because I have learned it and I continue to learn it every day. And if it weren't for the years of BODYshame and suffering I endured, I wouldn't be able to write these words to you with such passion and authenticity. I wouldn't be able to give these healing tools to you. Your BODYpeace journey isn't happening to you - it's happening for you so you can grow and learn more about yourself and then teach what you have learned to others. That's why we call this a discovery journey - not a ~~recovery~~ journey. ~~Recovery~~ implies there is something wrong with you. But, you're not broken. You don't need fixing, you need awakening. You need to awaken to the fact that this is really a process of shedding the layers of who you've been pretending to be, the molds you've tried to fit into, and discovering who you really are.

Channel Your Inner Soul Sister

Grab your BODYpeace journal and let's get crackin'!

Think of one to five addictive behaviors or negative thought patterns that you know are not serving you. Write down the answers to the following questions in day three of your journal:

- What is the addictive pattern/negative behavior?

- How do you know it's addictive and not serving you?

- How does this pattern/behavior make you

feel? What does it feel like in your body?

- How do you want to feel? How do you want to feel in your body?

- Ask the Universe to help you change this addictive pattern/negative behavior.

For example: "I am addicted to calorie counting. I feel like I can't stop counting calories. I know it doesn't serve me because it takes me away from what is truly important about the food - how it nourishes my body, how it energizes me, and how it makes me feel alive. I want to feel free and calorie counting makes me feel trapped. Universe, please help me change this pattern. I need your help. Show me how."

How did that go? It's tough to take a hard look at the patterns and behaviors we've caught ourselves in, but that is the key to setting yourself free. As long as you are in denial you stay in the dark. But when you come out of denial and shine an honest light on what's really going down for you, you can move through whatever you perceive is holding you back. You might be feeling a bit of guilt, shame, or anxiety over this. That's totally normal. It's important for you to feel that and to learn how to move through it, and we're going to do that now through forgiveness and surrendering.

Forgiveness is a key tool in your BODYpeace toolkit.

Without forgiveness, you're stuck in resentment and you're in denial of the BODYshame you're experiencing. You know what else begins with the letter "f"? Freedom. And it's no coincidence. Forgiveness is your direct flight to freedom. With forgiveness, you set yourself free from the cage you've put yourself in and snap yourself back into your truth.

So, now we're going to practice self-forgiveness with your Self-Forgiveness Meditation. I suggest practicing the act of self-forgiveness regularly. But this is your meditation to use at your convenience. You now have it at the tips of your fingers so just use it with your best judgment. If you're being unkind to yourself, having a super critical day, or are feeling guilty about something you ate, this meditation will really help you to release the resentment and negative feelings that you're carrying so that you can return the love that you are. You can access your Self-Forgiveness Meditation here: http://bodypeacemovement.com/book.

Now, get on your knees (yep, literally) and say to the Universe about each addictive pattern/behavior, "I am powerless over my addiction to _____. I surrender. Take this from me. Show me how to heal." Really milk this and take your time. Say it over and over and over again. If tears start to flow, let them flow. As you cry, you heal. Every tear represents an aspect of yourself that you are letting go. Crying is a roadmap to clarity. Just let yourself feel it all. Then, be patient and wait. Trust that the guidance will come to you at the exact moment that you need it.

How did your surrender moment go? What have you learned from this exercise? Head over to the BODYpeace Facebook community and share it with all of your BODYpeace sisters. We are all here to support you!

And one extra-important note here - from now on, when you catch yourself in the middle of a negative self-talk fest, or you're binging, purging, or obsessively counting calories, ask the Universe for help. Take a moment to invite the Universe to help you get out of BODYchaos and into BODYpeace. This is a super powerful step. So often, we don't ask for help because we don't know that invisible help is available to us, or we don't think we're worthy of receiving the help, or because we simply forget to ask. We always have the gift of free will - the option to choose. The Universe won't intervene until you ask and give it the green light. Give it the go-ahead, baby!

SOUL SCRIPTURE

When I'm in a state of BODYchaos, I ask the Universe to guide me back toward BODYpeace.

#BODYpeace

DAY 4
LET YOUR FEELINGS BE YOUR COMPASS

Remember what our good friend Jiminy Cricket said? "Always let your conscience be your guide!" I never got it when I was a little girl but now I know what he was saying: Let your feelings be your compass. Your feelings are your internal compass; they give you clear direction on the guidance you should follow. In other words, your inner soul sister speaks to you through your feelings. Your feelings are not just these senses that you feel within you; they're a form of conversation that your inner soul sister uses to get your attention.

You know what are really good numbing agents for our feelings? Food and exercise. Until now, you've used food and/or exercise to numb out all of the feelings you don't want to feel. You overeat because you are trying to avoid a feeling you don't want to feel. You over-exercise because you are trying to avoid a feeling you don't want to feel. You restrict your food because you are trying to avoid a feeling you don't want to feel. These numbing agents are used to distract you from feeling your feelings. As you try to numb out those feelings, you also numb out your connection to your inner soul sister.

Every feeling that you have needs to be treated with good ol' tender love and care. This is especially true for women. We make most of our decisions based on how we feel or how we want to feel. You overeat because you want to feel better. You restrict because you want to feel better. You over-exercise because you want to feel better. But now, instead of eating or exercising or restricting your feelings, your job is to become the non-judgment witness to your feelings. All day. Every day. Sometimes, the feelings are joy and happiness and abundance. Sometimes, the feelings are anger and shame and sadness.

It's not your job to try and push away the uncomfortable feelings with food or exercise - it's your job to let them in and let them be your teachers. It's your job to let your feelings be your compass. Behind every feeling is a lesson, and the uncomfortable feelings just so happen to hold the juiciest lessons. Once you learn the lesson, that uncomfortable feeling you were trying to avoid goes away. You feel like Joseph Gordon-Levitt in *500 Days of Summer*, on top of the world, skipping through the streets, dancing with the birds, and beaming at everything and everyone you see.

At first, when you let those uncomfortable feelings come up to the surface, you might feel like you're breaking down. But with every breakdown comes a breakthrough. After that breakdown, you receive the most amazing guidance and the most beautiful lesson. You get the breakthrough and you grow more into the woman you've always wanted to be - the woman you have always been.

Sometimes a feeling has to stick around for a while before we can understand what it has to teach us. Most of the time, you have to experience the feeling fully and then the Universe shows you the lesson. That's what makes the spiritual classroom different from the school classroom. In school, we're taught that we need to learn things before we can go out in the "real world" and experience them. In the spiritual classroom, it's the opposite - you have to experience things before you can learn them.

Channel Your Inner Soul Sister

Time to pull out your BODYpeace journal! Write down how you feel about your body right now. Be honest. When you are honest with yourself, you really gain the clarity you need to truly heal from the inside out. When I began my own BODYpeace journey, I felt ashamed of my body and disgusted by it. All I wanted was to change it. There was a part of me that just wanted to scream all of the words onto the page as a way to release all of the secret shame I'd been carrying around. That is what this exercise is for you - a way to get out all of the shameful things you think about your body but are too scared to talk about. Here is the time to do it and just let it pour out of you.

If you feel blocked and are unsure of where to begin, that's okay. In that case, just write this prayer down first: "I don't even know how to put words to how I feel about my body, but I am willing to be honest with myself. I know that when I am honest with myself I receive the clarity I am seeking much faster. Inner soul sister, help me to know the truth about how I feel about my body now so I can be that much closer to loving the body I already have."

Take three deep breaths and let your pen flow…

Now, it's time for part two - soul dreaming. This is one of my favorite exercises, and it's so great to do after you dump all of your shameful thoughts onto paper. After you do a brain dump like that, you hopefully feel that release. But now, it's time for you to take the power back into your own hands and create the vision of how you want to feel in your body. That is what soul dreaming is for. Soul dreaming is like daydreaming but with a clear intention behind it.

Soul dreaming, as Doreen Virtue says, is when you reach up to Heaven for your soul's desires and bring them down to earth. And what are your soul's desires? Feelings! Your soul doesn't care what you look like or how much you weigh. Your soul just cares about feeling good.

From your feelings, you can create visions of how you want your life to unfold. From your feelings, you create these soul dreams, which become the blueprints for how you really want to live your life. Let yourself get lost in your soul dreams. Today the intention behind your soul dreaming experience is the answer to these three questions:

- How do I treat my body when I think those shameful thoughts?

- Who would I be without those shameful thoughts? How do I want to feel in my body and what does that look like to me?

- What one change do I want to make by the end of this BODYpeace journey?

Ready? Press play on your Soul dreaming meditation, which you can practice at http://bodypeacemovement.com/book.

Now grab your notebook again and reflect on your soul dreaming experience. Write down every detail you can think of. Now you have a very clear idea of when your ego is doing the talking and when your inner soul sister is doing the talking. And, more importantly, you have your soul's desires for how you want to feel in your body down on paper. You can refer back to them at any point in time throughout your BODYpeace journey. You can add to it, and tweak it, as you go.

Now it's time to share your soul dreams! Share them by posting your biggest takeaway from the soul dreaming in the BODYpeace Facebook Group. Your sisters are waiting to support you!

My feelings are my compass, guiding me to my truth. #BODYpeace

DAY 5
BECOME SPIRITUALLY FIT

Just like we do certain physical exercises to strengthen our physical muscles, we do certain spiritual exercises to strengthen our spiritual muscles. Marianne Williamson, a magical woman and one of my spiritual mentors, talks about this concept a lot. It really resonates with Kasey and I because we love working out. Meditation, prayer, and journaling are your go-to spiritual exercises for making those spiritual muscles pop. When you're committed to your spiritual practice, you have built up mental strength to simply not react - to not act on impulse. This might seem kind of lame at first glance, but think about it. How many times has someone emailed you or texted you something and you knew you should have waited before hitting the send button? But you just had to get your word in. Or how about when someone asks you to hang out and you'd rather stay in? But the people pleaser within you forces you to say "yes" instead of taking a pause to check in with your inner soul sister.

These decisions might seem small, but they're the ones we make all day long so they're really the most important. They're the decisions that help make up who we are. The gift of waiting - of not reacting immediately - is a big one. When you act on impulse, you're acting from your ego. *A Course in Miracles* says, "The ego speaks first, and the ego speaks loudest." But when you give yourself the gift of waiting, you still allow your ego to have its two cents, but you also give yourself time to shoo it away and welcome in the guidance of your inner soul sister. When you wait for the guidance to come in, you receive exactly what you need.

The more you work your spiritual muscles, the stronger they become and the more connected you are to your inner soul sister. That means you have no problem putting the phone down for five minutes to check in with your inner soul sister and ask that question from yesterday, "What do I want to come of this?" This way you can more easily discern what is true for you verses what is true for the friend who texted you. When you are connected to what is true for you and make decisions from that space, you can ditch the people-pleaser and be that powerful woman who can unabashedly make decisions peacefully and fiercely.

Now, you might be thinking, "How is my impulsive nature with texting related to my disordered eating habits?" or, "How is my impulsive nature with my romantic partner related to my disordered eating habits?" Here's the deal, gorgeous - your relationship to anything is your relationship to everything. Your relationship to others is the mirror of your relationship to yourself. So, that impulsive desire to send that snarky text, or get that last word in during an argument, carries over to your relationship with yourself. When it's 9:00 p.m. and you know you're not hungry but you listen to that impulse to get off the couch, grab the bag of popcorn or pint of ice cream, and chow down while watching TV, that's acting on impulse too. Fine-tuning your spiritual muscles will help you slow down and hear the guidance from your inner soul sister.

The Universe has an answer for you the second you choose to still your mind and ask for help. Trust that whatever messages you are meant to receive, you will receive in perfect timing. Not on your clock - but the Universe's clock. And the Universe's clock is always way more accurate than yours. Have faith that you will receive the message exactly when you need it.

This is usually the point in time when you realize you've been having a spiritual fling with your inner soul sister for the past few days. You realize this spiritual stuff isn't just for shits and giggles. It's not about just reading it - it's about actually doing it. Once you realize you've been having a spiritual fling with your inner soul sister, you are now faced with the fact that you must have a full-on spiritual relationship with her. You can't be flighty. You have to be committed.

I remember my "oh shit" moment. At the beginning of my spiritual journey, I was so hooked on this stuff - like, totally obsessed. I wanted to soak up everything I could learn. I was so hungry for it. I felt so free and alive when I learned a new meditation or read a new book by a new-to-me self-help author. I couldn't wait to learn more and read more. As I dove deeper into these book, podcasts, YouTube videos, and lectures, I realized that wisdom without action was useless. This spiritual stuff couldn't just be entertainment for me. It had to become my life's practice. I realized early on that if I really wanted to master this stuff, I'd have to live it and experience it for myself. No amount of reading could change me. I had to change me. Check yourself. Have you been giving yourself a teaser of transformation or the experience of transformation? You can't learn to love yourself just by reading about it. You actually have to get dirty and do the work. You can only learn to love yourself if you are willing to learn who you are. And you can only learn who you are by getting quiet and cozy with your inner soul sister on a momentary basis.

Channel Your Inner Soul Sister

So what do you say, darling? Are you ready to end the fling and commit to a full-on relationship with your inner soul sister?

To do that, we need to put the serious stuff aside for a sec and invite more fun and inspiration into your days. The Universe wants you to be inspired and to have fun because both of those virtues help you cultivate BODYpeace. Part of the reason we get stuck in the BODYshame cycle is because a piece of us forgets how to laugh and have fun. When you are joyful and creative, you feel inspired and then you inspire others. Think about someone you love or admire. You just love being around them. Why? Because their joyful energy and presence inspires you! The way you generate that joy is by filling yourself up with creativity and what inspires you instead of filling yourself up with food. Your joy and creativity are your gifts to the world, and it's time to unleash them. When you unleash them, you feel more connected to your body, to your purpose, and to others.

Grab your BODYpeace journal. Really marinate in these questions, sister. Gift yourself the time and space to answer them with all of your heart and soul. There is no right or wrong answer. Just be honest. Remember, the more honest that you are, the more clarity you get.

Take a deep breath and center yourself with this prayer, saying it slowly to yourself with intention: "Inner soul sister, speak through me. Through this exercise, help me to harness my joy and creativity. Help me to have the courage to use these gifts to serve myself and others."

- What made you feel alive and connected as a kid?

- What makes you feel alive and connected now?

- What did you do for fun as a kid?

- What do you do for fun now?

- What makes you feel inspired?

This simple exercise is so great because you realize two things: 1.) you can learn a lot from your younger self and 2.) the things you used to love are usually what are missing from your life now.

Now, it's time to set your "I Love Me Date!" Of everything you just listed, pick the one that you feel most connected to. How can you easily make space for this in your life? Maybe you miss playing sports so you commit to joining a pick-up league. Or maybe you miss playing piano so you commit to dusting off the old keyboard once a week for a half hour. Choose a small, achievable goal that feels good that you know you can accomplish with ease. Put it on your calendar for the next month and write it as "I Love Me Date!" Commit to doing it throughout the rest of your BODYpeace journey. I promise you that this small tweak will get your creative juices flowing and will help you feel amazing!

You can choose more than one if you feel called to do so. Just make sure it's fun and not overwhelming for you. That way you're more likely to accomplish it! Whatever you choose, make sure it lights you up inside and feels good.

Bonus Tip - if you can't remember everything that lit you up as a kid, ask your friends and family. They'll be able to give you a lot of insight that you might not remember. Their memories of you are a great foundation for you to learn how you can inject more joy and creativity into your life!

My joy and creativity are my gifts to the world.

#BODYpeace

DAY 6
RENEW YOUR BODY VOWS

We can become so consumed with taking vows with a husband or wife that we forget about the most important vows we could possibly renew - our body vows. You can create your own body vows and renew them every morning with yourself.

Just like two people get married and become united, so should you and your body. Every morning, as you inch out of bed and mosey over to the bathroom, look in the mirror and renew your body vows with yourself.

When you're thinking loving thoughts and choosing only to have conversations of love around the body, your body will become more beautiful to you. The more you think with love, the more love you see. Your body will not become more beautiful because of what it looks like, but it will become more beautiful because of what it can do for you. What does your body do? It is an amazing vehicle through which you express love! You give and receive so much love with your body. Your inner soul sister is here to connect, to inspire, and to nourish yourself and others. Your body doesn't really have a purpose here - your soul has a purpose here. Your body is the house to your soul.

There is a beautiful lesson from *A Course in Miracles* called *The Holy Instant* which is characterized by "when an ancient hatred becomes a present love." In that moment when an ancient hatred ("I hate my body") becomes a present love ("I love my body"), we choose a loving belief over a limiting belief. This decision - this *Holy Instant* - creates a miracle, which is a shift in perception from a limiting belief to a loving belief. This miracle allows you to see your body with new eyes. The miracle is that you start to have a different experience in how you choose to see your body. Start to see your body through a soul sister's eyes instead of through your ego's eyes. Do this by reciting your body vows.

Channel Your Inner Soul Sister

Ready for one of the most powerful exercises ever? This will change your life.

Grab your BODYpeace journal and open it up to today's exercise. This beautiful blank space is here for you to write your own body vows. So, write 'em down.

What do you want to promise your body 'til death do you part? Just let your pen flow. Trust your wisdom, sister. There is so much of it inside of you.

When you're done, head over to your mirror and tape your body vows to your mirror. If you want to keep them private and don't want anyone else seeing them, that's okay. Just put them in a place where you will be able to see and recite them every day. This way, every morning, you will always be reminded of your truth.

Do it now! I'm serious. Head over to the mirror, energetically hold your own hand, look in the mirror, and recite them to yourself. You've got this! I know it might feel weird at first. That's totally normal. Just trust the process. As you continue to do this daily, it will become more natural and much easier for you.

We're so proud of you, sister!

Take a picture of your body vows using the hashtags #BODYvows and #BODYpeace. Tag me @HeatherWaxman and Kasey @KaseyArena! Post it in the BODYpeace Facebook group too. Share the BODYpeace love with everyone you know! By posting your body vows, you're encouraging other women to learn to love their bodies too. You are part of this BODYpeace movement. You are a leader!

SOUL SCRIPTURE

Dear body, I love you, I accept you, and I see you. I promise to cherish you all the days of my life. #BODYpeace

⊕ DAY 7
SOUL SISTER IN THE MIRROR

Today is the day you're going to get cozy with your mirror in a new way. Set aside some "me time" with yourself today and head over to your mirror. Take off your clothes and get naked. Yes. Press play on your BODYpeace meditation to open up the space for you to show your naked body the love it deserves.

As you stand in front of your mirror, slowly scan every inch of your body with your hands. Begin at the top of your head, your forehead, and then move to your eyes, your nose, your ears, your neck, your shoulders, your boobs, your stomach, your hips, your butt, your thighs, your calves, and your feet. Touch every inch of your beautiful body and, as you do, say, "I love you, _____" to each body part. I know it feels awkward at first. Just stick with it and remember why you're doing this for your beautiful body!

As you touch your body and say, "I love you," to each part of your body, know that it's safe to look at yourself in the mirror. I know how uncomfortable this might feel. I felt the same way when I did this exercise for the first time, and I thought it was a big load of bullshit. But then, it turned out to be so cathartic and healing. It was one of the greatest gifts I could have given myself - like another key to unlock the door to falling in love with my body. If you give it your all, I promise it will be that for you too. Be gentle with yourself and ask the Universe to be with you and help you harness the inner strength you need to do this.

Now grab your BODYpeace journal. Sit down and marinate on that experience. How did it feel to you? How did it feel to give yourself loving attention instead of negative attention? I remember the first time I did this exercise. I actually bawled my eyes out. It was such a healing and emotional experience for me particularly because I learned how little I really knew about my body. I'd never given it the TLC it needed, and I was never encouraged to get down with my bare, goddess self in front of the mirror. It was just not something I ever thought about. But it's something you should think about. The choices you make for your body reflect what you believe is the purpose of your body. That includes your choice to work toward loving your body exactly as it is now.

It is not dirty to touch yourself. It is not wrong for you to love being naked. It is a divine way for you to connect with yourself. That, my dear, is BODYpeace. Lift the veil of fear from over your eyes that has been preventing you from seeing the truth about your body. When you choose to lift the veil of illusions you've been telling yourself, all you see is the truth - and that truth is love. That truth is BODYpeace.

Your BODYpeace sisters are here to support you! Check in on the BODYpeace Facebook group and fill your fellow goddesses in on your experience with the mirror. You never know who needs to read your words of inspiration.

My body doesn't need to change — my thoughts about it do. #BODYpeace

DAY 8
YOU ARE NOT YOUR BODY

Can you remember the first thing you were taught about your body? What were you raised to believe about your body?

We're not taught how to love and accept our bodies - we're taught how to criticize them, abuse them, and change them. For as long as you can remember, you have believed that your body defines who you are. You have believed that the weight you're at, the clothes you wear, and the amount of makeup you slap on your pretty face all help to define you. All of those things are fine if they are used as an extension of who you are. When we use our weight, clothes, and makeup to make us feel better about ourselves, that's when we get lost. No matter how much you search, nothing outside of you can fill the big hole of BODYshame within you. Only love can do that.

The good news is this - when you choose to change your mind about the true purpose of your body, you start to perceive your body in a new way. In a true way. You see your body through spiritual sight, and with spiritual sight there is only one truth - you are whole.

Grab your BODYpeace journal. Now stop, drop, and breathe. Close your eyes and place your hands over your heart. Ask yourself, "What does my ego tell me is the true purpose of my body?" Take some time to think about it and write it down. Be honest with yourself. Remember that honesty leads to clarity. Write what you believe to be true for you right now, according to your ego.

Here's the deal, sister - you have a body, but you are not your body. Sounds kind of crazy, right? I get it. You've been taught the opposite for your entire life. But your body does not define you because it isn't who you are. Wayne Dyer mentions this in many of his talks and I love how he describes it. He says that the body he has today is not the same body that he had twenty-four years ago or even twenty-four hours ago. Our bodies are constantly shedding skin cells and are constantly in a state of change. Your body will change, but your soul is changeless. Your soul - the essence of who you really are - defines you. Your body will die, but your soul is deathless. Your soul is limitless. And so are you. You are limitless.

Your body cannot feel love - only your soul can do that. Your body is home to your soul. Your body is an amazing servant that cannot feel love, but it does house the love within you. Your body is an amazing vessel through which love can flow to you and others. That's what it means to say, "my body is a messenger of love."

Channel Your Inner Soul Sister

It's time to put on your spiritual glasses and start seeing things from a soul sister perspective. When you're tempted to make decisions for your body based on the calorie count, what will make you lose weight, what will make you gain weight, or what will help you tone up, that's a sure sign that it's time for you to stop, drop, and re-connect. In these moments, you're disconnected to your inner soul sister because you are forgetting about the true purpose of your body - to be a powerful vessel through which you let love flow into you and out to others.

To reconnect with your inner soul sister, first ask the Universe for help. A simple prayer like, "Universe, please help me move from BODYshame to BODYpeace" is perfect. Then, ask your inner soul sister, "How do I want to feel in my body when I eat food?"

Have you ever thought about that before? How do you want to feel when you're eating? Before your meal, how do you feel? When you're eating a meal, how do you feel? After you've eaten a meal, how do you feel? This is how we make eating a spiritual practice. Start making your food choices from that place instead of how many calories you're eating, or how much sugar a food has, and you will start to feel more peaceful, energized, and connected to your body. When you are spiritually fed, you are automatically physically satisfied.

Deciding how you want to feel at mealtime is another key ingredient to your BODYpeace lifestyle. Before you do that though, it's important to take a look at how you feel before, during, and after you eat. For example, maybe you feel anxious before you eat because you're afraid of feeling bloated or gaining weight after you eat. That anxiety follows you into the meal and stays with you through the end of it. Because you were unable to eat in a relaxed state, your body was unable to register the food it was eating. You were craving peace during meal time so your body tells you it's physically hungry. But, you just ate so you can't be physically hungry! You're spiritually hungry. Your body isn't starving for food - it's starving for peace.

A good indicator of how you want to feel during the meal is often the opposite of how you feel when you eat now. If you feel anxious and out of control, you probably want to feel peaceful and calm during your meal. Maybe you feel sluggish after meals, so set a goal to feel energized after the meal. These are called your BODYpeace feelings.

Now that you've figured out how you want to feel, ask yourself this question: "What do I need to do to reach a state of [insert feelings here] with my food?" So, if your goal is to feel peaceful and calm with your food, maybe you start your meal off with a prayer to bring you into that peaceful state. If your goal is to feel energized after the meal, then maybe you choose to make food choices that will help you feel alive and energized after you've eaten instead of sluggish and weighed down.

When you stop eating your feelings, and start eating in alignment with your BODYpeace feelings, your relationship with food expands into a very loving one.

Now, a really obvious feeling we get from food is pleasure. Because I spent so many years restricting my food intake and associating food with misery, one of the feelings that is important to me is pleasure. If I don't feel pleasure with my food while I'm making it, while I'm eating it, and after the meal, I notice that I feel an urge to grab another snack, or an urge to binge. This isn't because I'm hungry or lacking nutrients. It's because my inner soul sister didn't get her need of pleasure met and she's still seeking it. What does pleasure look like for me? It depends. But, I've nestled into some pleasure staples like warm oatmeal with raw vanilla protein powder, peanut butter, cinnamon, stevia, and almond milk for breakfast. For lunch - a big, creamy, hummus-filled salad with a baked Japanese yam. Some days, pleasure comes in the form of coconut milk ice cream or an order of fries. And some days I want cereal for dinner. But what matters most is this: When I'm connected to how I want to feel, I have faith that my inner soul sister will guide me toward the foods I want to eat most of the time and the foods I want to eat some of the time.

A Course in Miracles says that every situation is a relationship and that includes your relationship with food. Your BODYpeace feelings are the gateway for you to form a loving relationship with food.

Now that you've done the work, it's time to share it! After you've written them down, share your BODYpeace feelings with the BODYpeace Facebook group. Give yourself big props for how far you've come! This is such a big turning point in your relationship to food.

SOUL SCRIPTURE

I will be free when I no longer identify myself as a body. #BODYpeace

DAY 9
SEEING YOUR BODY WITH NEW EYES

It's time for you to see your body with a fresh pair of eyes. We are switching our primary vision from physical sight to spiritual sight. We're taking off our body-bashing glasses and putting on our BODYpeace glasses. When you put on your BODYpeace glasses, you can see that you are already perfect. You can see that you are not broken. You can see that you don't need to be fixed - you need to be awakened.

Awakening is the result of choosing to see things in a new light. When you let the light (the truth) in, you awaken to a whole new perspective about your body. Awakening is the byproduct of the miracle. When you experience the miracle (the mental shift in perception from fear to love), you intuitively see things from a new perspective. You can sense that nothing physically about you has changed - but you feel a very clear change has happened within you. It's the sense that you have evolved, you've grown, and you've emerged.

Now that we're more than one week into this, you've probably experienced many moments of awakening. That is amazing! With every moment of awakening you experience, you'll find that you feel a deeper sense of BODYpeace.

When you have your BODYpeace glasses on, you look past someone's physical body and into their soul. You look into their eyes, the windows to their soul, and focus on their inner light as you chat with them. Your soul communicates with their soul, producing perfect vision.

We're not denying your gorgeous body here. Think of what an amazing servant your body is! Think back to all of the mental and physical wear and tear it has experienced. And yet, all your body has ever done in return is love you back. No matter what you've mentally said to it, or physically done to it, it's continued to work for you as best as it can. It has continued to carry you where you need to go. What an incredible servant your body is for you!

We get tripped up when we overvalue the body and undervalue our inner soul sister. We place more emphasis on looking hot and getting skinny than we do on listening to our inner soul sister's guidance. And that's when we get lost... because there is no purpose in looking good and getting skinny. When we do place our sense of worth in looking good, or getting skinny, or gaining muscle, we feel like we lose a sense of purpose. It's not that you've lost your sense of purpose. It's still there. You just forgot what the purpose of your body is - which is to be a vessel of love.

When you start to switch your sight from physical sight to spiritual sight, you start to recognize that purpose. You feel at home in your body because you are reconnecting to the true purpose of your body.

Your body's eyes cannot see all of the miracles that you experience every day, but your mind's eyes - the eyes of your inner soul sister - can see it all crystal clear. That is perfect vision and it is available to you now. You just have to want it, open yourself up to receive it, and it's yours.

Channel Your Inner Soul Sister

You ready for this, sister? Of course you are. It's time for you to put your light working skills into action! With every person you meet, look at that meeting as an opportunity to bless them and recognize the light in them. Every person you come into contact with gives you an opportunity to see them with new eyes - to put on your spiritual glasses, look past their physical appearance, and choose to honor the love that lives inside of them.

A Course in Miracles says, "When you meet anyone, remember it is a holy encounter. As you see him, you will see yourself...for in him you will find yourself or lose yourself." Soul sister translation - when you choose to first honor the love that lives inside of you, you're not only helping yourself along your BODYpeace journey but you're also helping whoever you come into contact with own their light too. We are all connected. We are not separate bodies talking to one another. We are souls within bodies talking to one another. So when you choose to honor the love that lives inside of others, you find yourself. When you choose to judge someone else, you lose yourself.

Journal about an amazing encounter you had with

someone today. How did you recognize their inner light, and how was that reflected back to you? Maybe you gave the barista at your local coffee shop a little extra love by asking her how her morning was going. And maybe in return, she smiled and thanked you in such a genuine way that you felt a connection you hadn't felt in a while. Every encounter is a beautiful assignment for you to extend and receive love and light. That's you being a light worker in action!

SOUL SCRIPTURE

I choose to see my body through the eyes of love.
#BODYpeace

DAY 10
BYE-BYE COMPARISON TRAP

I used to be the queen of comparison. If Comparison was a city, I would have been the mayor. If they had Comparison's Anonymous, I probably would have gone to it. I was addicted to comparing myself to others. It was almost like I got high off it. The temporary high of trying to puff myself up and make myself better than others was accompanied by the inevitable low of, "Her thighs are so much thinner than mine" or, "Her cheekbones are so pronounced, and my cheeks are chubby and ugly." The cycle was endless. I felt like a hamster constantly spinning my wheels, getting nowhere fast. Even though comparing was so harmful to myself, I felt like I couldn't give it up. When I had my defining moment of spiritual surrender, I knew that I had to be willing to give up comparing if I wanted to start to learn to love myself and create a life of BODYpeace.

I realized that I had to create a new conversation around my body if I wanted to stop comparing myself to other people's bodies. And that conversation couldn't have anything to do with what my body looked like. That conversation had to be about what my body is here to do and the woman I am here to be. That conversation had to be about the purpose of my body according to the Universe, not the purpose of my body according to Hollywood. For me, that meant ditching the magazines and the celebrity gossip. Anything that yo-yo dieted between glorifying a curvier body and glorifying a skinnier body was out the window. I tossed all my magazines and stopped watching celebrity gossip news.

When you compare, you get nowhere. When you love, you get everywhere.

You see, the more we make a curvier body more special than a thinner body, or a thinner body more special than a curvier body, we create more separation from each other. Love creates truth. Comparison creates separation. When we create separation we get further and further from the truth of who we really are, which is why you always end up feeling like crap after comparing yourselves to others. This is why our society, at large, has such a screwed up viewpoint on bodies. We haven't really gotten down to the truth, have we? If we'd gotten down to the truth then there wouldn't be this separation, and we wouldn't have an image-obsessed culture. If we'd gotten down to the truth, everyone would see themselves through the eyes of BODYpeace.

You don't need a magic pill, diet plan, or fitness routine to make it all better. All of that is just throwing a Band-Aid over the wound. And we all know that Band-Aids only last temporarily. You don't need to become a pro at eating cleanly or working out to achieve BODYpeace. You need to be become a pro at managing your thoughts about your body. *A Course in Miracles* says, "Do not ask Spirit to heal the body. Ask rather that Spirit teach you the right perception of the body." Can you imagine what would happen if people all over the world started saying, "There's nothing wrong with my body. But there is something wrong with the thoughts that I have about my body. That's really what I need to change."

Are you showing your body conditional love or unconditional love? Conditional love says, "I'll love my body when I lose ten pounds," or, "I'll only have this BODYpeace stuff down when I'm eating the perfect diet." Unconditional love says, "You know what? I like to eat lots of plants. But chocolate also has its place in my life and can be an act of self-love. And that's perfectly okay." Unconditional love says, "I know I planned to go to the gym today, but since my intention is to feel peaceful in my body, I think I'll go to the movies by myself tonight. That will make me feel truly peaceful today." Unconditional love says, "I know I just ate half a bag of popcorn. Instead of punishing myself, I choose to forgive myself. Inner soul sister, please help me forgive myself and understand why I chose to numb out with popcorn."

In order to love your body later, you have to start loving the body you have now. Moment by moment, redirect your thoughts to unconditional love. What does that mean? It means being really gentle and really compassionate toward yourself as you shift your thoughts from limiting to loving. It means feeding yourself words of BODYpeace instead of feeding yourself words of BODYshame. Remember - you can't self-hate yourself into self-acceptance. You have to self-accept yourself into self-acceptance. How are you doing?

Channel Your Inner Soul Sister

Be really patient with yourself on this one. I still compare myself too (it's a hard habit to break). But the number of times I compare myself to others has drastically decreased and, most importantly, when I do compare myself to others, I no longer believe that it's truth. That's all because of my strong commitment to BODYpeace. I know you're committed too, or you wouldn't have made it this far.

I remember listening to a recorded lecture given by a brilliant public speaker. She was so loud, vocal, and outspoken. It started to piss me off and I started to spew attack thoughts at her like word vomit: "She's so loud and obnoxious!" "She doesn't listen to anyone else when she talks...she just likes to hear her own voice!" "She is so self-absorbed and that's why she can talk so loudly and obnoxiously!" I stopped myself and realized the person was none of the insults I'd just spewed at her. She was a lesson for me, and my lesson was to work on fine-tuning my own ability to speak my truth firmly and with love. When I witnessed this, I was able to turn it around and recognized that I actually admired her for everything I had thought I hated her for.

Jealousy shines the spotlight on the parts of your life that need a tune up.

Today, be your own private investigator and start getting to the bottom of how often you compare yourself to others. When you're comparing yourself to other people, you're doing it because that jealous part of you believes that person has something that you can't have. That causes you to feel helpless and project your jealous thoughts onto them, feeding your ego's belief that it will make you feel better. The reality is that we are all equal. We are all capable. We are all spiritual beings having a human experience, which means we all have the infinite love of the Universe inside of us. We are extensions of the Universe, and we are infinitely capable of creating a happier life experience.

When you catch yourself feeling pissed because someone has something you think you can't have, or are incapable of having, feel it. Honor the jealousy and be with it. Then, when you're ready to release it, flip your script. You don't actually hate that person. You aren't actually jealous of that person. You actually admire them. Yes! Eureka! You don't hate your BFF for lighting up a room when she walks into it and getting all the attention. You admire your BFF because you see that possibility in yourself too. You don't hate that girl with strong muscles at the gym. You admire her dedication and strength because you know that you have the potential to be dedicated and strong too. That admiration is nudging you to see the same possibility in yourself.

Turn your jealousy into admiration today with these four

action steps.

Every time you catch yourself throwing down jealousy, follow these four steps:

WHAT JEALOUSY CAN TEACH ME

OWN IT

Own the fact that you're being a crazy, jealous person. Just witness the behavior happening and try not to judge yourself. As Maya Angelou says, "If you'd have known better, you'd have done better." Where do you feel it in your body? Breathe into it deeply and just witness where it is in your body.

FORGIVE YOURSELF

Forgiveness is like taking a hot bubble bath of love and compassion. When you notice those comparison thoughts coming up, choose to forgive yourself. You can simply say, "I am acting like a crazy, jealous person. I know this isn't real. I choose to forgive myself." Follow it up with a laugh. Laughing at yourself always helps. I mean, it is kind of funny how nuts it is, huh?

PERFORM A TUNE UP

Recognize that your jealousy is shining the spotlight on an area of your life that needs a tune up. Ask yourself, "What area of my life needs a tune up here?"

FLIP YOUR SCRIPT

Now that you realize the person is illuminating an area in your life that needs a tune up, thank them. Yes. Thank them for being your teacher and helping you to create positive change in your life. What is it that you admire about this person? Honor that, and be thankful they helped you illuminate that part of you.

You've got this, gorgeous! Don't forget to check in with everyone on the BODYpeace Facebook group. Tell us how you turned your jealousy into admiration and what you learned from it! Or, just out yourself. Whatever you need, we're here to support you. We're in this together!

SOUL SCRIPTURE

When I compare, I get nowhere. When I love, I get everywhere. #BODYpeace

DAY 11
THE ENERGY IN MY FOOD

Well, hello there, my soulful friend! Today, we're going to take our exploration a bit deeper and dive into the energetic connection between you and your food.

Energy is in everything. Energy is in me, energy is in you, energy is in your cell phone, energy is in the chair you're sitting on, energy is in this book…energy is everywhere! Quantum physics proves this. It teaches us that everything is made up of subatomic particles which, when broken down, become a vibration that we refer to as energy. At the deepest level, everything is made of energy. That means - you guessed it - there is even energy in your food. So what does energy have to do with the connection between you and the food that you eat? Simply put, it means this - the energy you bring to your food is the energy that you are ingesting.

I'll give you an example. Something I tended to do was rush through preparing my meals and rush through eating my meals. I used to think of prepping my meals as a disruption to my day and I felt the same way when I ate my meals. Instead of seeing my meals as a form of self-care, I saw eating as an unwelcomed interruption to my day. I saw cooking and eating my meals as disruptors to time that I could be doing something "more productive." Even though I loved food, I didn't honor its purpose for my body, and I didn't honor the time my body needed to process that food.

I always felt this sense of anxiety and frantic energy when I ate my meals. That's the energy I brought to prepping my food. From the first slice of sweet potato, I wasn't present. I was rushing and speeding through the prepping process as fast as I could and, because of that, I came to resent prepping my meals. That rushing, frantic energy, therefore, carried through to my meal, causing me to eat too fast and be really absent from my meal. I was always puzzled after the meal because, even though I was physically satisfied, I felt emotionally unsatisfied after the meal and I'd feel triggered to have another snack or binge. Finally a light bulb went off for me - as long I was spiritually hungry, I would never truly feel physically full. I was unsatisfied after eating because I wasn't bringing peace and presence to my meal.

Your meal doesn't start at meal time. Your meal doesn't even start before the first slice or spoonful of ingredients. Your meal starts with the energy you are bringing to that first slice or spoonful. This is when I realized I needed to become more aware of my BODYpeace feelings, not just at the dinner table, but all the time. As I became more aware, I realized that I plowed through my meal because there was this underlying thought of, "There isn't enough food to go around," lurking through my mind. I felt like I had to shovel everything I could into my mouth...as if the food was going to disappear if I didn't eat it right then and there. As I questioned this thought of, "There isn't enough food," I realized it was deeper than that. It stemmed from a limiting belief that I was holding onto: "I am not enough." Because I believed I wasn't good enough, I believed that taking time to enjoy my meal was selfish. How could I invite more self-care into my life when I believed I wasn't worthy of it? This was such a powerful realization for me. Can you relate?

When I had this realization and noticed how I'd been mentally treating myself, I had so much compassion for myself and I wanted to treat myself better. A few simple shifts allowed me to gradually become more present, aware, and peaceful at meal time, and I noticed my body respond kindly. For starters, I began thinking about how I prepared my food. Cooking honestly isn't something I love to do, so I realized that I needed to make it more fun so that I could become more present and look forward to it. I started taking my time cutting the veggies and injected fun into the process by playing some music, listening to a podcast, or putting on an episode of one of my favorite TV shows. I stopped eating while I was cooking so I could actually sit down and enjoy my entire meal instead of eating half of it standing up. I'd pray before my meal to continue to bring that peaceful energy to the table. And then, I'd make my meal fun! I'd light a candle, continue to listen to some soothing music, or just create an environment that felt fun and pleasurable to me (and yes, for me, sometimes, that means TV). That helped me to start to enjoy the sensory experience of my food by tasting my food and noticing the different textures.

Choosing to bring a new, fresh energy to my meals has

given me a heightened appreciation for my body, and I've gotten to know my beautiful vessel so much better. Now, I have a much more spiritual connection with my food. I look forward to prepping my meals, and I look forward to eating my meals, because I changed my energy and customized mealtimes to become fun for me. Now, it's your turn!

Channel Your Inner Soul Sister

The energy you bring to the meal is the energy that you eat throughout the meal. Take a mental inventory of your personal eating process. What eating habits are you currently engaging in that aren't serving your soul? What eating habits are serving your soul? Commit to becoming more conscious of this and, instead of looking at cooking as another item on a never-ending to-do list, start seeing it as an act of self-care for you to fine tune the gorgeous instrument that is your body.

Now, think about the energy you're bringing to your meals from prepping time to eating time. What energy do you bring to your meals? Take some time to mull it over and write it down. Be as specific as you can. The more specific you are, the more clarity you will get on what you know needs to change. What energy do you want to bring to your meals? How are you going to do this?

As always, your ideas are so much more powerful when they are shared! Post your triumphs, trials, and nuggets of wisdom on the BODYpeace Facebook page. This is your community.

SOUL SCRIPTURE

My soul will always tell me what is best for my body. I just have to breathe and listen.

#BODYpeace

DAY 12
REMOVING SHAME FROM YOUR DIET

I've mentioned the word BODYshame quite a few times already and it will continue to pop up throughout the book. Why? Because, according to Brene Brown, a professional shame researcher, shame is directly correlated with addiction and eating disorders.

Brene Brown perfectly describes the difference between guilt and shame. She says, "Guilt is 'I made a mistake' and shame is 'I am a mistake.'" Guilt says, "Oops. I made a mistake for eating more than my body needed." Shame says, "I am a mistake for eating too much."

When you mentally abuse yourself like that, you are calling yourself a mistake and a bad person. This keeps you stuck in a BODYshame prison and you feel like there is no way out. In response to that, we compulsively overeat, and then feel guilty for overeating. So continues the BODYshame spiral. Sound familiar? It does to me. I knew it all too well.

What I've come to learn through my own experience, and through studying Brene Brown's research, is that BODYshame has its own herd of commandments. These commandments aren't the ones that will bring you freedom. These commandments are the ones that will keep you stuck and small.

BODYshame says, "Nope, you can't find BODYpeace. You're not good enough."

BODYshame says, "Why are you even bothering? You never finish anything."

BODYshame says, "How can you possibly achieve BODYfreedom when you just binged on a whole bag of kettle corn last night? You're such a hypocrite."

BODYshame says, "You have to be nice to people all the time, you have to look thin while you do it, and you have to appear modest while you're at it."

BODYshame says, "Screw your intelligence and your soul. The number one factor that is most important is how you look. Your appearance will always matter most."

BODYshame says, "You have to say, 'I'm sorry,' when you don't understand something."

At the core of all this BODYshame, is this one belief Brene Brown articulates gorgeously. BODYshame says, "Do it all, do it perfectly, and never let them see you break a sweat."

Isn't that it, sister? You put so much pressure on yourself to be perfect, to do it perfectly, and to execute it all without letting anyone see you flinch. I used to be this way too. But here's the thing - that is not reality. You are never going to be perfect according to society's standards, but you will always be perfect in the Universe's eyes. It's not that you aren't perfect, it's just that you've bought into the wrong definition of perfect. Instead of thinking that you have to do certain things in order to be perfect, what if you started to come from the belief that you already are perfect? At your very core - at the seat of your soul - you are perfect. There is nothing wrong with you. You are not broken. You don't need fixing. You need awakening. You need to awaken to this new lease on life - one that is free of BODYshame and filled with BODYpeace. And today, that means you are willing to let go of BODYShaming yourself regularly.

This endless web of perfectionism that we get trapped in manifests in the all-or-nothing relationship that we have with food.

BODYshame says, "Ugh, well, I just had ice cream in the middle of the day. I might as well binge on that chocolate that's been hiding in my cupboard too. And a huge bowl of cereal won't hurt either."

BODYshame says, "Because I was 'bad' yesterday, I'm going to make up for it by being 'good' today."

Now, these thoughts are pervasive throughout not just our minds but also the minds of countless other women. Our goal isn't to ignore them or stuff them down. Our goal is to acknowledge these BODYshame thoughts and then use our BODYpeace tools to move through them.

Channel Your Inner Soul Sister

Pick a BODYshame thought that you had today. Choose any one that you want. Then challenge it. We are so quick to believe our BODYshame thoughts. We let them take us down instead of stepping into the room with them and challenging them.

Challenge your BODYshame thought by asking, "Is this really true?"

So, if your BODYshame thought is, "I was bad yesterday," challenge it by asking, "Is this really true?"

When I examined my own BODYshame thoughts and asked myself, "Was I really bad yesterday?" I found that I wasn't bad at all. I was trying to cope in the best way I knew how. I didn't have the BODYpeace tools I have now so I tried to numb out all the pain, anxiety, stress, and fear I was feeling. And it worked. Food does the job! Not forever though, and it doesn't feel particularly peaceful, but it does temporarily do the job. Challenging my BODYshame thoughts allowed me to shine a compassionate light on myself and to see, at the end of the day, I truly was doing the best I could with what I had.

BODYshame, as Brene Brown says, survives in secrecy, silence, and judgment. When you keep your BODYshame thoughts a secret and hold them silently within you, you become your own worst enemy. That's why the BODYshame spiral continues - because the endless swirl of self-judgment perpetuates. That is, until it is outed. When you let your BODYshame out of the closet, you free yourself from the BODYshame shackles that have held you down. If you want to live a BODYpeace life, you must share your BODYshame.

So, this is your soul work for today:

- Write down five BODYshame thoughts you had today.

- Challenge them. Ask yourself, "Is this really true?" and give yourself concrete examples of why the BODYshame thought is a BODYlie.

- Shine a compassionate light on your story. How can you find compassion for yourself?

- Share your BODYshame story with your BODYspace soul sisters and ask for their support in helping you squash your BODYshame spiral.

SOUL SCRIPTURE

If we can share our story with someone who responds with empathy and understanding, shame can't survive.

~ Brene Brown

#BODYpeace

DAY 13
BLESS YOUR FOOD, BLESS YOUR BODY, HEAL YOUR APPETITE

PART I: BLESS YOUR FOOD, BLESS YOUR BODY

If our bodies are here to be vessels of love, then what is the purpose of food? From a soul sister's perspective, food is a tool for you to learn to love your body. It is a tool for you to connect more deeply to your vessel of love. If you think of your body as the vessel, food is the oxygen. It helps you feel vitality. It can help you not just live but actually have the experience of feeling alive.

If your body is a vessel of love, then you want to keep that love flowing by putting foods into it that align with love - foods that will support the loving life force flowing through your precious vessel. The loving foods for you might be different from the loving foods for me. These days, loving foods tend to be simple vegetarian foods like oatmeal, quinoa with veggies, veggie omelets, or tempeh with roasted Brussels sprouts and some Japanese sweet potato. Sometimes, loving foods are a glass (or two) of sauvignon blanc, a big bowl of coconut milk ice cream, fries, chicken or turkey, or a big bowl of Puffins cereal while catching up on my Netflix. It's all the same to me because I eat in accordance with my BODYpeace feelings.

How do you know if a food you want to eat is a loving choice for your body? You bless your food and your body before you eat. It sounds so simple - and it is - but it's also so effective. This simple blessing over your food and your body will help you become present with the food, and that is what allows you to figure out whether the food you are about to eat is aligned with your BODYpeace feelings or not.

Before every meal and snack, take time to bless your food and your body. This will center you, balance your emotions, and help you eat slowly and more mindfully. It can also help to reduce your cravings and will help you savor the food that's nourishing your body. Say this blessing before you chow down and watch your meal experience shift: "I bless this food. I bless my body. I bless what this food can do for my body. May it nourish my mind, may it nourish my body, and may it nourish my spirit. Thank you."

So simple, right? You can do that. Even if you're out to eat, you can do it. If I'm out to eat, or having a dinner at a friend's house, I will take a breath and repeat it silently before digging in. If someone asks you what you're doing, tell them the truth. "I'm blessing my food because it helps me eat more mindfully." When people see how peaceful you are and how you're savoring the food, they'll want in on it too.

Channel Your Inner Soul Sister

Before every meal and snack you eat today, say this prayer. Allow the words to seep into every cell of your beautiful being. Say them slowly and let them nourish you just as much as the food you eat.

PART II: HEALING YOUR APPETITE

I was really inspired by Doreen Virtue's talk called *Healing Your Appetite, Healing Your Life*. Doreen Virtue is a master communicator with the angels and teaches others how to connect with the angels. This lecture found me when I was in a really tough spot one night, feeling super triggered to binge. The anxiety I felt over the urge to binge was almost unbearable but I really didn't want to go down that road of numbing out my anxiety. I recognized my anxiety and wanted to use my spiritual tools. I placed my hands on my heart and asked my inner soul sister, "What would you have me do? How can I manage this anxiety right now?" I heard my inner soul sister tell me to go to iTunes and search for Doreen Virtue. So I did...and I stumbled upon this awesome audio lecture from her. I listened and took notes like a crazy woman and found so much peace in everything she said.

Your appetite is an instrument that measures the amount of peace of mind you have. Doreen says, "When we lose our peace of mind, our appetite tends to remind us." I loved hearing her phrase it this way because it helped me feel less crazy, and it helped me be able to reframe the insatiable anxiety that triggered me to binge eat. It reminded me of the fact that my body and my soul are in constant communication with each other and, when my soul isn't satisfied, it can use my body to remind me of that.

From now on, think of your I-want-to-binge-right-now-appetite as your body's way of telling you that you have lost your peace of mind. Instead of feeling like you have no control over the insatiable I-want-to-binge-right-now-appetite, consider it a sign for you to dig into your spiritual toolbox and use your BODYpeace tools to help you get to the root cause of what's going down.

We have a basic instinct to maintain peace of mind. When we feel like we are not able to maintain that peace of mind, or feel like it has been threatened in some way, we hear a voice say, "If you eat this food, you will feel better." And we might - but we'll only feel better temporarily. Why do you get into this crazy cycle? Because you are eating over your inner soul sister's guidance. When you hear or feel guidance that might challenge you, or bring up resistance, you reach for food to try to avoid following your inner soul sister's guidance. Here's the deal - there isn't a piece of chocolate in the world that can drown out the voice of your inner soul sister.

Overeating, restricting, binging and purging, and compulsive eating are delay tactics. They help you do two things: put off for the future that which your inner soul sister is telling you to do now, and numb out the BODYshame that you're feeling inside.

Four feelings trigger you and they are fear, anger, tension, and shame (which, as Doreen points out, just so happen to spell out the acronym FATS). When you feel triggered to go to a dark place of binging and purging, overeating, or restricting, use the acronym FATS and ask yourself, "Am I feeling fear, anger, tension, or shame?" When you figure out which one it is, go to a sacred space of yours (or just get really still), and have a soul chat with the Universe. Put on your soul dreaming meditation and repeat one of the affirmations below over and over. Keep repeating it until you feel a shift occur within you. Then, ask your inner soul sister to help you release whichever FATS you are feeling and patiently wait for the guidance.

Affirmations for Releasing Fear:

• I am at home in my body. Fear is a stranger here. (*A Course in Miracles*)

• Help me let go of fear and help me let in love.

Affirmations for Releasing Anger:

- When I think I am angry at someone else, I am really angry at myself. Universe, help me to witness why I am angry at myself and show me how to release it.

- I am willing to treat myself with compassion instead of anger. Universe, show me how to do this.

Affirmations for Releasing Tension (Anxiety):

- I am feeling tension, but I know there is peace in every breath. Universe, help me use my breath to connect back to peace.

- I breathe in peace. I breathe out tension. (Repeat this for 90 seconds)

Affirmations for Releasing Shame:

- I am willing to let go of this shame. Universe, help me to release it.

- I know that shame survives in secrecy. Help me muster the courage to share my shame with someone I trust so I can release it and move forward.

• I am ready to remove the baggage from the past and replace it with excitement for what the future holds.

So, gorgeous, I ask you this: What are the FATS in your schedule delaying you from - writing that book, signing up for that yoga class, or starting that blog? Get honest with yourself and start making this your evening ritual. Why the evening? Because that's probably the time when you most feel triggered to binge. You have more things to distract yourself with throughout the day - work, school, errands, etc. - but at night, that's when shit gets real and the voice can no longer be drowned out by your daily activities. So at night, when your pesky ego wants you to binge, grab your journal, pinpoint which FATS are clogging your psyche, and free write about it. Then, say your affirmation while playing your soul dreaming meditation as a call to Spirit to help you release it. And most importantly, take action! If you're feeling fearful of starting your own blog or taking that yoga class, don't just witness it. Try saying affirmations over it. You have to take action along with it! Part of the reason you're overeating, and part of the reason these FATS are clogging you up, is because you are procrastinating taking action on something. Your introspective soul work is imperative, but it's also important to honor that calling within you. That is what will set you free.

Channel Your Inner Soul Sister

Take a mental inventory of the FATS that are holding you down and triggering you to control your food through overeating, restricting, binging and purging, or compulsive eating. Choose the one that is the most prominent for you. Write it down and then choose one of the affirmations that resonates most with you. Repeat that affirmation to yourself as you play your soul dreaming meditation and ask Spirit to help you release whichever one of the FATS is keeping you clogged.

Then, write this at the top of your page: "What is one action step I can take right now to release this _____ (insert fear/anger/tension/shame)?" Now, close your eyes, place your hands over your heart, and ask your inner soul sister this question. Breathe deeply, and patiently wait for an answer. If you're having trouble listening to your guidance, put on a song that makes you feel connected to her (your BODYpeace and soul dreaming meditations are great options!), or use your notebook and let your inner soul sister communicate to you through your writing. You will be amazed at the guidance that comes through you. Trust it whether it seems too simple or totally whacky and out there.

Trust your soul's guidance.

Got it? Great! Post your action step in the BODYpeace community to hold yourself accountable! Remember - ideas are more powerful when they're shared because you're calling on the support of like-minded people to include space for you and your visions too.

Be patient with yourself and trust the process. Remember that every moment you choose to change your mind about this situation, every moment that you choose to use your spiritual tools, is a miracle. Honor every single one of those miracles as stepping stones along your BODYpeace journey.

SOUL SCRIPTURE

I bless my food. I bless my body. I bless what my food can do for my body. #BODYpeace

DAY 14
TAP YOUR WAY TO BODYpeace

Yesterday we chatted about getting to the root cause of your triggers. Today, I want to give you an amazing tool that you can have at your fingertips all the time - particularly when you feel panic-stricken from your trigger to binge or after looking in the mirror and hating on what you see. Witnessing your behavior is amazing, and journaling and meditation, as you've now learned, help you discover so much more about your authentic self. But sometimes we need to dig even deeper - and tapping is an awesome way to do just that. No, I'm not talking about tap dancing (although that's rad too). I'm talking about tapping as in Emotional Freedom Technique (EFT).

Not too long ago, I was feeling like I'd hit a wall in my own discovery journey. I had reached a pinnacle in my journey and I was feeling all of these super intense emotions. I knew I was on the verge of a huge breakthrough...but it came disguised as a relapse. Before big breakthroughs, we often have big breakdowns, and it can sometimes look like a relapse. But it's actually the Universe's way of saying to you: "Hey, guess what? You're SO close to a big breakthrough! Let's detox all of the old shit that's not serving you really fast so you can come out on the other side really fast." You feel me?

This happened to me a few weeks into writing this book.

I knew that in order to be a truly effective teacher, I had to not just be a teacher of BODYpeace but also a masterful goddess of BODYpeace. I had to fully embody the message of BODYpeace and I had to live and breathe it with every fiber of my being. The only way that I could do that was to detox every aspect of my own life that was associated with my disordered eating habits. Every remnant - big and small - of my eating disorder had to go. So, one morning I sat down in front of my homemade altar and had a chat with the Universe. "Okay," I said. "I'm ready to let go of every single aspect of my life that is connected to my eating disorder and is keeping me stuck in the cycle of BODYshame. I know that in order to be a masterful goddess of this work, I have to learn how to deal with it all. So, I'm ready." I heard my inner soul sister say to me, "Are you sure you want this?" And I emphatically said, "Yes, I'm 100% sure."

And, it came...in many BIG tidal waves. In the coming weeks, I felt SUPER out of control. It felt like every single detail of my life that was not serving me was magnified. The Universe gave me no choice but to put the magnifying glass on everything that wasn't working...but I couldn't just inspect it. I had to dive into the experience headfirst. To be honest, I felt like I was in a tailspin. All of my tools were just not working for me. I felt anxious and I felt like I was spinning out of control. So I prayed for a miracle. In other words, I asked my inner soul sister to help me change my mind about the situation and to guide me to heal these massive, painful blocks.

A few minutes later, tapping popped into my head. I'd heard of tapping before and it had been recommended to me before but, for whatever reason, I wasn't receptive to it until that moment. I knew that was my inner soul sister's way of saying to me, "Girl, learn how to tap ASAP." And as Spirit would have it, tapping started coming up everywhere! I was seeing it all over the internet, I saw the books on display, and I heard people referencing it. I couldn't get away from it! This is how the Universe works - when you make a request, it will give you a solution. It might not be what you expected, but it will be exactly what you need. If you choose to keep your eyes and ears open to the signs, they will be everywhere.

I started to research tapping and began using it when I felt triggered, anxious, panic-stricken, stressed, and angry. I was amazed, astounded actually, because in those moments when you feel out of control or totally stressed out to the nth degree, you just can't sit down and meditate or journal. You're in such a heightened state of stress that you need a quick and effective tool to move you out of the chaos and into the calm. That is what tapping will do for you.

I've put together two videos for you: one explaining what the heck tapping is, and the second is a tapping session for when you feel totally stressed out and triggered. That moment when you want to run to the freezer and grab the ice cream - do this tapping video. That moment when you want to snag the bag of kettle corn from the top shelf of your snack cabinet - do this tapping video. That moment when you're stuck in traffic and you're starving, and all you can think about is going home to binge - tap on it. That moment when you are so stressed out that you feel like nothing else will work - tap on it. Seriously - it's that transformative. This particular tapping session is for when you want to overeat or binge, but you can always change the setup statement to adjust it to whatever is going on for you.

Now, sit back and watch the lowdown on what tapping is. Then let me guide you through a tapping session. You might notice your ego piping up and saying, "You don't need this," or, "This is so lame." Or you might be feeling a lot of resistance in general to doing it. That's fine. Do it anyway. Remember, the stronger a call is to your soul's evolution, the more resistance you will feel. Lean (and breathe) into the resistance and follow along with me.

Have a notebook handy to free write about your first tapping experience and then share it with the BODYpeace Facebook group! You'll also see the tapping script below in case you'd rather go through the session on your own.

Check out the tapping videos that help guide you on http://bodypeacemovement.com/book.

If you're digging the tapping conversation, I highly recommend reading *The Tapping Solution for Weight Loss and Body Confidence* by Jessica Ortner. It's a really amazing resource to accompany BODYpeace!

"Resistance is a sign that you're ready to change." #BODYpeace

DAY 15
EATING IN THE LIGHT

You can't change who you are by changing what you eat. I used to think I could do that. I would starve myself and desperately try to change my body, thinking it would make me feel happier, confident, and more complete. But the more food I restricted and the more weight I lost, the more lost I felt. I came to the realization one day while looking in the mirror, picking at my stomach, and checking to see if I had a thigh gap, that no matter how many calories I ate and no matter how many hours I logged at the gym, I couldn't change who I was. I'd been trying to change my body, yes, but that was a cover-up. What I was really trying to do was change who I was at my core. I hated the fact that I was sensitive. I thought that made me weak and I, therefore, felt like I could never fit in. I abused my body to try to numb out the shame I felt over who I was. All of this helped me awaken to the fact that I was doing it all backwards. I wasn't here to change who I was - I was here to accept who I was. It was time to stop trying to make myself invisible and it was time to muster up the courage to let myself be seen.

Sister, you have spent so much time using food to try to change who you are - using food to make your thighs smaller, using food to get washboard abs, using food to make the number on the scale go down.

This is how you think: EATING LIGHT + WEIGHING LIGHT =

HAPPIER ME.

Here's the real equation: EATING IN THE LIGHT = HAPPY ME.

Beneath that external search to change your physical body is an internal search to change who you are. You've been trying to change the essence of who you are because a piece of you believes that she isn't good enough. My dear BODYpeace sister, you have nothing to change except your thoughts about yourself. You have nothing to lose except your thoughts about your body. You have nothing to lose except your thoughts about food's purpose for your body.

You're used to focusing on eating light - the less calories, the better; the less fat, the better; the less carbs, the better; the less sugar, the better. What if you shifted your focus from eating light to eating in the light? Because that's who you are. You are a divine spark of light, and when you eat foods that are grown in the light, you are eating in the light. And when you eat foods that make you feel like that divine spark of light that you are, you are eating in the light. And that is when you start to truly fall in love with your body. When you eat in the light, you light the spark within you that says, "I am ready to love my body in this new way - in this true way - because I get it. I understand now that my body is this miraculous vessel that I use to help heal myself and help heal others."

That is what you're here to do and that is who you're here to be. That is your purpose in this body in this lifetime.

You are here to heal yourself and heal others, and food is one of many tools you can use to heal yourself.

Channel Your Inner Soul Sister

Now it's time to get into the practice of eating in the light. But, as *A Course in Miracles* says, "You cannot bring the light to the darkness; you must bring the darkness to the light."

Before we can fully embrace eating in the light, we need to get familiar with the foods that keep us eating in the dark. What foods trigger you to binge, overeat, restrict, and over-exercise? What foods do you only eat because you consider them to be "diet foods"? Which foods do you eat because you think you should? Which foods do you eat because you've learned that they're "healthy"? This isn't about you eating "cleanly" or eating "perfectly." This is about you determining what foods make you feel like you're eating in the dark and which foods make you feel like you're eating in the light.

Head over to your BODYpeace journal. Open to a blank page and draw a line down the middle to create two columns. On the left, write "Eating in the Light" and on the right, write "Eating in the Dark."

For the foods that keep you eating in the dark, check yourself. It's not the food itself that is the problem - it's why you're choosing to eat the food. Go through each one and ask yourself, "Why does this food trigger me?" There is no wrong answer here and it might take some time to come to you. Always remember to place your hands over your heart, take deep breaths, and check in with your inner soul sister. Maybe you are addicted to sugar and love the high of the sugar rush. Or, maybe there is a specific memory that you associate with a food and that memory triggers you to overeat. It can be a myriad of answers. Commit to getting clear on this and it will give you the freedom that you're seeking.

If this exercise feels too restrictive or too challenging for you, think of it this way - you're taking the power away from the food, and you're taking the power back. You are choosing to eat in the light. That means choosing with your free will to distance yourself from food that makes you feel dead and in the dark and gravitating toward foods that make you feel alive and in the light. When you're done with this list, you should feel like a weight has been lifted from your shoulders and that you have a roadmap of foods that will help you to truly eat in the light.

Instead of focusing on eating light, I focus on eating in the light. #BODYpeace

BODYfuel

From Starvation to Satisfaction

YAY! You made it to day sixteen! It's Kasey here, and I am excited to help you continue your BODYpeace journey.

The next fifteen days are all about food. We will be releasing our fears about food and embracing it in a new light - one that fuels your body rather than restricts it.

Food is fuel. It's as simple as that. Should I just stop writing now? Obviously I wouldn't leave you hanging, but it's amazing to me how such a simple concept can be taken to such extremes.

For so long, I looked to everything outside of myself to make me happy...when the one person I needed to look to was me.

Do you ever feel tirelessly lost and confused when it comes

to food? Do you find yourself asking, "How many calories do I need? Should I only be eating 'healthy' foods? Can I never eat another french fry?" Without realizing it, these words like "only" and "never" are total extremes of such a simple equation.

Personally, I've been through many extremes when it comes to food. I've lived a life of food restriction, which was rooted in always wanting to have "control" over something. If you read my initial story (which I sure hope you did!) you learned that from a young age, control and I have had our struggles.

After graduating high school and entering college life, this change started to bring up some anxiety similar to what I dealt with as that little fourth grader.

My four years at college were a big transition time in my life, as it is with most new students. I had school, work, friends, family, more responsibilities, projects, meetings, and was squeezing in some fitness.

When I was younger, controlling the foods I ate, the times that I ate them, and the combinations of foods I ate at meal times made me feel better. It numbed my anxiety. Even after years of therapy, with this new transition into college, the anxiety began to rear its head and body image issues began to stake claim in my mind.

The thought then became, "How can I manipulate this food to make my outward appearance look a certain way?"

In college, my normal breakfast consisted of a big bowl of cereal. And for lunch I usually had nothing. Dinner (after an hour of cardio at the gym and doing a thousand crunches) was a bowl of rice and steamed veggies. I would sometimes snack on trail mix at night if I wanted something sweet. At this point in my life, I was all about being as thin as I could be.

Looking back, the fact that my disordered eating habits started to come up again doesn't surprise me. I was going through a lot of changes, and as you may realize, I didn't adapt to change very well.

While all of these uncontrollable things were happening, the two things I did have 100% control over were food and fitness.

During my sophomore year, I joined the track team. However, I was still struggling with body image and inner fears of gaining weight and being not good enough. There were some days when, if I felt like we didn't get enough cardio in at a practice, I would sneak into the gym and jump on the elliptical. Even typing that now makes my heart hurt because I remember that feeling, and know that people still struggle with that feeling of "not doing enough" or, wanting to burn more calories to reach a certain ideal they choose to buy into.

The rest of that year, I was still obsessing over my outward appearance because of this underlying feeling of not being good enough. When my junior year hit, I decided to no longer be on the track team. I found myself losing the love for it - but really, I was losing love for myself as an athlete.

I got a job at the gym and focused more on my health and physical education major, which was exciting for me! I always wanted to teach and I loved to help others, so this seemed like a great route to take.

At this point, no longer being on a sports team, I decided to take on a new challenge and compete in my school's body building and figure show.

I honestly fell in love with weight training that year. I LOVED lifting, challenging myself, and working out on the elliptical machine. I decided to compete without having any knowledge of how to fuel my body or train properly for a show. I made up my own program, went with a cookie cutter restrictive diet, and listened to what other people were doing - like cutting out carrots because they had "too much sugar."

Again, I found myself comparing my body to others and striving to look just like them, completely losing sight of me. Before I knew it, I was on a 1200 - 1300 calorie diet with hardly anything other than meat, brown rice, sweet potatoes, two tablespoons of almond butter (that were measured perfectly), protein shakes that consisted of just the powder and water, and green veggies. Why? Because I thought the only way to attain happiness and to "feel good enough" was by attaining this outward appearance I so ardently sought after.

I would restrict my calories, exercise for hours on end, and then binge one day a week on foods I had restricted myself from the week prior.

I thought I was only "allowed" to eat healthy foods and then, one day a week, I would go buck wild on a bag of trail mix. I was so wrapped up in these thoughts that I believed thirteen grams of carbohydrates from a quarter of a cup of oatmeal was a high carb day, and I couldn't even think of picking up a banana until after my show was over.

Sometimes we do these things to ourselves without even consciously realizing what we are doing - not only physically, but mentally as well.

So, here I am in 2012 when I first competed:

This is what I was doing:

- Living off of less than 1200 calories a day.

- No fruit.

- 1-2 TB of nut butter a day (and I licked the spoon absolutely clean).

- No variety in my diet.

- Eating a "cookie cutter" diet (minus eating actual cookies).

- Obsessing over the amount of cardio I did.

- Almost passing out in one of my classes in college when I bent over to pick up a softball due to my lack of breakfast that morning.

No amount (or lack thereof) of body fat was going to make me feel any better. I was in a deep struggle on my journey to BODYpeace.

During this time, I may have lost twelve pounds, had those beloved abs I so longed for, and had visible muscles for the first time, but guess what? When I looked in the mirror, I STILL was not happy with my body.

But, wait, I finally had everything I wanted, right?

Wrong. If you haven't caught on yet - this lean version of myself wasn't what I was truly searching for. I was searching for BODYpeace and looking in all the wrong places.

I remember looking in the mirror and picking myself apart thinking, "What can I change? Do I need to do more cardio? Do I need to drop my carbs?"

What people don't see when they look at my competition pictures is that:

- I lost my period due to my body fat percentage being too low to support a healthy menstrual cycle.

- My hair was thinning and falling out.

- My nails were beyond bendable.

- My digestive system was so out of whack that I suffered from pains daily.

- And pooping? Yeah, that wasn't happening.

Yet, when others look at those competition pictures from that day, they don't see what was happening on the inside - they see this outward appearance that many people strive for.

Talk about a constant mind game, right?

I think we all have different stories that have consistent themes of restriction, worry, control, and losing that sense of BODYpeace. Throughout this time, I was still struggling to find myself as Kasey Arena and looking to outward things to feel whole inside.

I started blogging because, during that time, I was attempting to get creative in the kitchen with the foods I was allowing myself to eat. I was in this battle of wanting to try new things that I was inspired by in the blog world but, basically still sticking to the same foods I felt comfortable with. Hence that pesky "control" issue sneaking its way back in.

I look back and am so thankful I started sharing recipes because that was my true passion coming through. Even though I was restricting myself, that glimmer of hope and passion was there and never faded away.

We know ourselves better than anyone, right? We have that little voice inside of us that can lead us to right or wrong. It's up to us to take into account what that voice is telling us.

I knew I wanted to pursue something with fitness, and I knew I absolutely loved helping people. I loved to train, lift, and challenge myself. My gut knew it was time to do this to be strong, glowing, and vibrant, full of energy, and not just to look a certain way on the outside. It was time to work toward finding BODYpeace.

I knew I needed to create a healthier relationship with

myself in order to really serve others in the best way I could.

At that moment, of meeting myself where I was, and not trying to be anyone else, change started to happen.

And guess what? It can happen for you, too.

Our goal with this book is to share our stories honestly in hopes that no matter what you're going through, you can use our guidance to help find your own BODYpeace.

Now let's get on to the fun stuff - food!

How to Embrace BODYfuel

Let's talk about BODYfuel, shall we? Sounds a lot like the word beautiful, doesn't it? I love that because fueling your body is beautiful.

I used to fear fats and carbs and only ate certain types of protein. My diet was so limited that it's no wonder I developed some intolerances to certain food. I was eating them daily without much variation due to my fear of eating unhealthy and gaining weight.

For example, I used to literally restrict my raisin intake because I thought, "Oh no! Carbs are bad and I can't eat too much of them or I'll get fat."

Don't get me wrong, I am all for eating healthy foods and having a strong foundation in nutrition, but whenever a goal starts to head toward an extreme, it's time to check yourself before you wreck yourself.

The only true way I was able to get over my food fears was to challenge myself to incorporate more of the foods I feared into my life. This, over time, helped me develop self-confidence and get over my constant fear of not being good enough. So often I see people cutting out categories of macronutrients, which are simply carbohydrates, fats, and proteins, or the three primary sources that make up our daily food intake. Our bodies thrive with a balance of all three that works for us, but too often people cut out a whole macronutrient to lose weight.

I believe, regardless of whether you feel you need to lose weight or you just struggle with food addiction, keeping all of the macronutrients in your daily intake is very important for BODYfuel.

Whenever I was struggling with fears of fats or carbs, I knew the only true way to enjoy them again was to challenge myself to eat them and prove to myself that my fears were not real - just a belief that I chose to invest in because of what people around me said.

I know that might create some resistance inside of you, but that's totally normal. The more resistance you feel, the more you know that you have to follow it.

Challenging myself with things like upping my fat intake, upping my carb intake, and branching out with protein choices really helped me realize how to add in more BODYfuel. I found that it wasn't weight I gained, but strength and happiness, which helped me fall in love with my body.

I learned that I could eat a greater variety of foods and not be afraid to enjoy foods in moderation that I once deemed unhealthy, which led to a whole new outlook on food in general.

Although all of us require a different calorie intake (note - my point with this book is to not get crazy with calories), when I finally took the time to research what my body truly needed in order to sustain my active lifestyle, I was amazed at how much I didn't even realize I was under-eating.

Our bodies are smart, and there are moments when you may feel hungry but suppress it or ignore it because you've chosen to buy into that wretched mantra: "Nothing tastes as good as skinny feels." Let's take a step back for a second. When you aren't giving your body fuel, you go workout, break down your muscles, and deplete the glycogen (energy) stores in them. How do you expect your body to perform at its highest capacity when you have literally depleted your body of energy and haven't refueled properly?

We all have been brainwashed by society, fashion magazines, and celebrity gossip to think that we need to restrict our calories so low in order to achieve an ideal that doesn't exist.

Calories don't just go in and out based on how many you burn after a workout. Think about how many muscles are working in our bodies on a daily basis! We need our heart to beat, our lungs to expand, our eyes to blink, and our brain to function...and how do all of these work? Fuel.

Fuel = energy = calories.

Now, excuse me as I put on my Health and Physical Education Teacher hat.

You're like a car...and you can choose whichever car you'd like to be. Vroom, Vroom!

Now, how does a car go? What does it need? FUEL.

What happens if it doesn't have enough fuel?

It doesn't make it very far, does it?

Ladies, it's as simple as that.

Isn't it amazing how many diet books can be written in extremes based off that simple concept?

I believe in going back to the basics to rediscover BODYpeace. By that, I mean going back to the basics of fueling the car that is your body to make it run efficiently, go farther, and carry your valuable things inside of it from place to place.

FUELING YOUR BODY = BODYfuel

My goal with all this car talk is to help you know that there is no one-size-fits-all approach to eating. I've been able to help myself without being obsessive about it. I believe there is a difference between being aware of our needs and being obsessed with them.

I've been able to enjoy foods that I once restricted myself from because they were unhealthy in my mind. I am not saying you need to obsess over calories, but I am saying that our bodies - especially if we're active, training, working, running, walking, blinking, thinking, and breathing - need fuel in order to do these everyday things. Often times, we are in need of more fuel than we think we are.

I am not saying that you need to track every calorie or become obsessed with numbers. What I am saying is that I hope you take the time to research and find a happy balance for yourself between what you need to eat for vitality and what you want to eat for pleasure. And there's no reason you can't have both all the time!

You can have a chocolate bar if you want it, without eating four of them in a half hour, and not feel guilty about it. You can have your ice cream, without feeling guilty, while still fueling your fitness, and lifestyle, with nutrient dense foods to get your vitamins, minerals, fiber, fats, carbs, and proteins.

I've found that if you tell yourself you have the freedom to enjoy what you want, instead of telling yourself that you can't eat a food ever or you can only binge on it once a week, you feel lighter and happier, and a sense of BODYpeace washes over you.

I don't enjoy seeing people hate on their fitness journeys because they think it has to be only one way or the highway. Or they think restriction is the only way to go in order to achieve their personal goals.

Exercise should be fun and enjoyed along with cooking, baking, and eating food. It is a tool we use to become stronger, not just physically but mentally too. Exercise helps our heart, lungs, legs, arms, and brain function more efficiently. Problems arise when we use exercise for vanity instead of vitality.

The truth is - information can be overwhelming, and comparing your lifestyle or food choices to someone else's creates a full-on mind war. We need to work together to start loving ourselves more and stop trying to think someone else's diet or fitness routines are the keys to our own happiness.

Every day, we are faced with a choice to either respect our bodies for what they can do or go against what our bodies are telling us.

Even though I may not be 100% recovered, I can say with confidence that whenever I started to finally give myself BODYfuel, love myself more, and look in the mirror and see that I am way more than a number on the scale, I became stronger than I'd ever been. I weigh about twenty five pounds more than I did in the competition pictures and I'm happier and healthier, fueling my body but also eating foods that I once thought I couldn't - in a balanced moderation that works for me.

I make sure that I eat enough to sustain my energy and performance. I try not to live by a rule book that I made up in my head.

I can't tell you what BODYpeace means to you, but I can guide you there. And that is what Heather and I are here to help you do.

You are more than capable of living a life of enjoyment instead of living your life in restriction. Life is about living. Life is about thriving.

Fifteen Days of BODYfuel

Now, try not to take this and think, "Okay, I'm going to go run and eat every food I've been restricting for the last couple of years and then burn it all off on the treadmill." Take small steps to getting back to your balance. What happens when you commit to small daily steps? You add them up to create one big transformation.

We will have a BODYfuel check - in after I challenge you to embrace food as fuel with recipes I've created. I will help you move through your food fears while challenging you to try new recipes and teaching you simple facts as to why they are important.

When I mention food fears, I don't mean being afraid of slimy green globs of goo (although I do have a delicious green smoothie recipe in here), but I do mean challenging yourself to try new carbohydrates, fats, and proteins. I am asking you to be willing to let go of your food fears as you try new recipes with me.

Throughout my years in the fitness industry, I've seen and been through food fears - fearing fats and carbs, fearing eating after 7 p.m., fearing eating at certain times of the day. All of these fears were based on ideas that I'd heard in the media, not from listening to my body. Whether you're a vegetarian, pescatarian, carnivore, dairy lover, vegan, kale junkie, or kale hater, these recipes will totally fit into your lifestyle.

The only way I could get through my food fears was to challenge myself each week, starting with small goals, and writing them down. For example, writing out my honest struggle of "I'm afraid to eat fat" and then writing down different fat-filled foods that I wanted to enjoy but was too afraid to.

All fat-filled foods were fears of mine: avocado (hi, guacamole!), hummus, nuts, nut butter, seeds, peanut butter, coconut, coconut butter, coconut oil, butter, olive oil, etc.

After writing out my fear and the foods I was afraid of eating, I worked to incorporate these foods into my daily meals. After scooting myself outside of my fat-free comfort zone, I realized that my body felt so much better when I started to give it what it wanted!

Throughout these next fifteen days, I challenge you

to work through your food fears and try new things. Don't forget - you have the BODYpeace Facebook group for 24/7 support.

If any of the recipes make you feel uncomfortable, awesome! That means you're challenging yourself to venture outside of your comfort zone and that's a key part of your BODYpeace journey.

The main goal of enjoying these recipes is to learn that food is fuel, and fuel is what makes our car (body) run smoothly. Once you really find peace with food as fuel, you are one giant step closer to BODYpeace.

DAYS 16 - 18
CARBOHYDRATES

For days sixteen, seventeen, and eighteen, we are going to talk about the importance of carbohydrates... which always go right to your thighs and midsection, right? WRONG. There's another extreme word, "always," sneaking in again.

A common diet myth says that limiting carbohydrates in your diet can help you lose weight and improve your health. Truthfully, the number of calories you eat and burn on a daily basis is what determines your weight. Carbs = energy, fuel, and muscle support. Ingesting carbohydrates is not a bad thing. Especially before or after a workout to boost your energy and help rebuild and repair your beautiful muscles!

The energy from carbohydrates is mostly used for normal bodily functions such as your heartbeat, digestion, brain function, breathing, and body movement. Cutting all carbs can be a quick fix but, in the end, it is an extreme method that is not sustainable (and makes you really cranky!)

Why do people fear carbohydrates? Well, as with most food fears, it usually comes from the myth that a certain macronutrient will make you gain weight. It's important for you to take a step back and realize that overdoing any type of food causes your body to get out of balance and into trouble. Remember what I said about myself? I cut out carbs and fat and felt like I was going to faint on a daily basis - all in the name of being thinner. Little did I know, I was destroying my body by not giving it what it truly needed.

Now, everybody is different. Some people handle certain macronutrients differently than others. That's why being true to you is so important, so you can cater to your own body's needs.

DAY 16
SCRAMBLED ROSEMARY POTATO HASH BROWNS

Scramble Ingredients:

4 oz. (or so) of organic firm tofu, or 3 eggs

Chopped up:

Peppers

Tomatoes

Red onion

Spinach

2 tsp minced garlic (or to taste)

Old Bay seasoning to taste

Dill weed to taste

Fresh pepper to taste

Chopped green onion for topping

Hash Brown Ingredients:

2 potatoes of choice, washed and chopped

2 TB coconut oil (or other high heat oil)

2 TB fresh, chopped rosemary

Sea salt and pepper to taste

Directions:

1. Spray or add oil of choice to a stove pan.

2. Add your chopped veggies and garlic to "cook down" for a few minutes on medium heat.

3. Once the onion is caramelized, add your other scramble ingredients to the pan.

4. Sauté on medium heat for about 8-10 minutes until all cooked together.

5. The tofu, or eggs, will soak up the flavors and cook up nicely in the pan. Again, this could be done with any type of protein: eggs, chicken, beans, or seafood.

6. While this is cooking, add your coconut oil to a separate medium heat pan.

7. Add in your chopped potatoes, fresh rosemary, sea salt & pepper.

8. Cook for about 20 minutes or until potatoes are tender & golden.

9. Combine both of these lovely recipes together for a great, balanced power meal of carbohydrates, fats, and protein!

BODYfuel Challenge - Have this traditional breakfast for dinner! Does having a breakfast meal for dinner, or vice-versa, make you at all anxious since this is out of the norm?

DAY 17
BLACK BEAN BROWNIES

Black beans and chocolate? A combo that would have freaked me out in the past since part of my "rules" was to not mix "unlike" foods. BUT, once I tasted these and didn't even realize the ol' legume was in there - I was hooked!

Ingredients:

1 15 oz. can black beans, well rinsed and drained

2 large flax eggs (2.5 TB flaxseed meal + 6 TB water)

2 TB coconut oil, melted (or another oil of choice)

¾ cup cocoa powder

¼ tsp sea salt

1 tsp pure vanilla extract

½ cup of sweetener granules of choice OR

   ½ banana mashed with some drops of liquid stevia.

1 ½ tsp baking powder

* I also like adding 1 tsp of dried coffee powder - it really brings out the cocoa flavor!

*You may need to add a little more cocoa powder if batter is too wet.

Directions:

1. Preheat oven to 350 degrees.

2. Lightly grease an 8 x 8 pan.

3. Prepare flax egg by combining flax and water in the bowl of the food processor.

4. Pulse a couple times and then let rest for a few minutes.

5. Add remaining ingredients and combine until smooth. *using a food processor will help the smoothness.

6. Add into your greased pan. Optional: Sprinkle with crushed nuts or chocolate chips!

7. Bake for 20-25 minutes or until edges start to pull away from sides.

8. Remove from oven and let cool for 30 minutes before removing from pan.

The insides will be a bit gooey - it's all good! Fudgey brownies = amazing, right?

BODYfuel Tip - Store in an airtight container for up to a few days and refrigerate!

DAY 18
SINGLE SERVE OATMEAL RAISIN CHOCOLATE CHIP POWER COOKIE

(with Chia Chocolate Sauce!)

Cookie, party of 1? When you make this…there is no guilt allowed for not sharing. Or, just double the recipe for a party of TWO!

Cookie Ingredients:

½ cup rolled oats

1 spoonful of chia seeds

1 egg (or 2 TB flax mixed with 3 TB warm water for a "flax egg")

¼ cup coconut milk

½ mashed banana (I snacked on the other half)

2 squares of chopped, unsweet baking chocolate (because I love bitter chocolate but you can use whichever kind you like!)

Spoonful of raisins

Cinnamon

Splash of vanilla

Few drops of liquid stevia or sweetener of choice

Directions:

1. Preheat oven to 350 degrees.

2. Mix all Ingredients together.

3. Put onto a greased or lined cookie sheet.
4. Bake at 350 for about 12-15 Minutes.

   While that bakes, mix your Chia Chocolate Sauce.

Chia Chocolate Sauce Ingredients:

1 spoonful of chia seeds

2 TB cocoa powder (I used dark)

A few drops of liquid stevia coconut milk (small amount)

Directions:
1. Add your chia, cocoa, and stevia into a small bowl.
2. SLOWLY add small amounts of coconut milk into the bowl, as you mix, until it's a nice, thick consistency. The amount can vary but it usually ends up being about ¼ cup to ½ cup.
3. Let it sit to thicken (the chia will help this) as the cookie finishes baking.

BODYfuel Tip - Once the cookie is out of the oven & cooled a bit, top with ice cream of choice, chia chocolate sauce, and some homemade coconut whipped cream (you'll be introduced to that soon!)

BODYfuel Check - In - How do you feel after these three carb-focused days? Did you feel some new energy from giving those muscles what they deserve?

DAYS 19 - 23
FATS

Fats totally make you fat, right? Um, let's try that again. Fats totally make your skin glow, nails strong, hair soft, and they help you. Fats help you maintain steady energy, reduce inflammation in the body, and maximize nutrient and vitamin absorption from the other foods that you eat.

Yet, some fear peanut butter like it's a pot hole they're about to ride their bike into.

I, myself, struggled with eating enough fats, which led me to have so many problems. My hair got thin and the ends snapped off like icicles, my skin got dry, I had next to no energy, and my body started to break down. My body needed fats in order to absorb nutrients from other foods, increase my energy, and repair my dry skin, brittle nails, and breaking hair, yet I was afraid of it.

For days nineteen through twenty three, we're going to become really FAT together: Focused, Aware, and Transformed.

DAY 19
ROSEMARY & OLIVE OIL ROASTED NUTS

A friend of mine makes these every year for our Holiday gift exchange - and I cannot get enough of them! They are the perfect snack with the best flavor combo. PLUS you get that FAT into your day!

Ingredients:
1 TB finely chopped fresh rosemary
1 TB extra-virgin olive oil
¾ tsp kosher salt
Sprinkle of black pepper
1 (10 oz.) bag whole almonds or nuts of choice (about 2 cups)

Directions:
1. Preheat oven to 325 degrees.
2. Combine all ingredients in a medium bowl; toss to coat.
3. Arrange nut mixture in a single layer on a baking sheet lined with foil.
4. Bake at 325 degrees for 20 minutes or until lightly toasted. Cool to room temperature.

You'll want these every single day...just saying.

DAY 20
ROASTED RED PEPPER & ZUCCHINI FRITTATA!

Don't ditch the yolk, yo! One of the biggest "fat fears" out there stems from the yolk of an egg. Now, if you don't eat eggs - no biggie! Remember the no judging rule throughout this book? Try adding in a new fat today and sharing it with us in the Facebook support group!

A little yolk lovin' for you:

- Each egg yolk contains seven vitamins: B6, folate, a B vitamin, B12, A, D, E and K. Of those, vitamins A, D, E and K are found only in egg yolks and not in egg whites.

- In fact, egg yolks are one of only a handful of foods in which vitamin D is naturally found.

- Egg yolks contain more vitamins - and larger quantities of those vitamins - than egg whites.

Ingredients:

2 medium zucchini

3 large eggs

2 TB oat flour (oats ground up!)

¼ cup chopped green onions

¼ cup chopped roasted red peppers

1 ½ tsp chopped fresh basil or oregano (or combine half of the 2!)

Sea salt & pepper to taste

Oil for cooking (I love using coconut oil for higher temps!)

Directions:

1. Rinse the zucchini, grate and place in a colander. Drain for 15 minutes, then squeeze to remove any remaining excess liquid.
2. In a large bowl, mix together the eggs, chopped roasted red pepper, green onions, basil, salt, & pepper. Add the drained zucchini and mix well.
3. Heat an 8 inch heavy or nonstick frying pan over medium-low heat and add just enough oil to cover the bottom of the pan.
4. Pour the batter to cover the base of the pan.
5. Cook the frittatas until they are golden brown on one side and set in the center.
6. Gently flip the frittatas over and lightly brown the other side.

Enjoy with some hummus to switch things up or top with some crumbled feta! Not an egg eater? We've got you covered! Try adding a can of drained chickpeas, ½ cup of roasted red peppers, sea salt, pepper, & a few TB of olive oil to make a homemade & nutrient dense roasted red pepper hummus!

DAY 21

COCONUT MILK WHIPPED CREAM

Coco-nutty for coconuts? I sure am. I used to fear coconuts because of their fat content, and then I realized not only how much I love the flavor of coconut, but also the nutritional boost that it gives our bods! Plus - any smell that reminds me of the beach is a good smell in my book.

Ingredients:
1 can of full fat coconut milk
Sweetener of choice

Directions:
1. Pop your can of coconut milk into the fridge (keeping closed) over night.
2. In the morning, take out your can and flip it over! Why? The liquid will separate from the hardened coconut cream in the can.
3. Flip your can back over and pour out the liquid. (Save for smoothies!!)
4. Next, add your cream into a chilled bowl and whip until creamy with a hand or stand mixer.
5. Add sweetener of choice and you are ready to enjoy on top of anything! Or by itself, of course!

Add your whipped cream onto your Power Cookie

& make sure to save some to top tomorrow's Avocado Chocolate Mousse!

DAY 22
AVOCADO CHOCOLATE MOUSSE

Combing avocado and chocolate in the same meal would freak the old Kasey out - but now it's one of my favorite desserts!

Ingredients:

2 TB cocoa powder

2 TB chia seeds

½ of a ripe avocado

½ cup or 1 cup (depending on how thick you want it) of coconut milk (from the carton!)

A few drops of hazelnut liquid stevia or regular sweetener of choice

Directions:

1. Add all ingredients into a blender.
2. Mix until combined.
3. Let sit for a few minutes and it will thicken nicely!
4. Top with whipped cream - optional but delicious.

DAY 23
OLIVE OIL DRESSING OVER A MIXED GREEN SALAD

Ever find yourself ordering fat free everything? Or squeezing a lemon on your salad when you truly want some olive oil and vinegar? Why not allow ourselves to enjoy a full fat dressing in a balance that works for us? Our bodies will thank us for bringing in the nourishing fats that help us utilize our fuel.

Ingredients:
2 TB extra-virgin olive oil (something I used to steer clear of during the food fat fear)
2 TB vinegar of choice (I like raw apple cider vinegar! It helps with digestion too!)
1 TB Dijon mustard
Squeeze of fresh lemon juice
Salt and pepper to taste
Few drops of liquid stevia or sweetener of choice to balance the flavors

Directions:
1. Simply combine ingredients and mix with your favorite greens and veggies!

SO simple! I love serving this over my packed salads to help with nutrient absorption! Did you know fat helps shuttle the nutrients from veggies into your beautiful bod?

FAT Check - In - How did incorporating more fats make you feel? How did you feel before and after the meal? Write it out and let the pen flow! Take your time.

BODYfuel Check - In - Are you feeling any more focused, transformed, or aware now that your body has received the fats it needs to thrive? I promise, if you continue to challenge yourself to incorporate more of the fats, your body and mind will thank you!

DAYS 24 - 26
FRUITS

Fruit = sugar = weight gain.

If you're catching my sarcastic drift, we're going to try this again.

Fruit = micronutrients = vitamins = FUEL.

Yes, people fear fruit. Why? Well, instead of seeing the benefits of ingesting these vitamin-packed powerhouses, people sometimes only see fruit as carbs, or "sugar." And often, "sugar" is a fear for people.

Fruit is nature's candy, full of an alphabet of vitamins and fiber and a quick, easily digestible choice for a pre-workout energy source. So why not include these tasty foods into your daily BODYfuel?

DAY 24
CHIA JAM

Your Chia Pet just got a new makeover and it just so happens to nourish hair health! Chia seeds are packed with nutrients like fiber, fats, and protein to fuel our bods while also giving your insides a nice squeaky clean finish. Chia Jam was actually one of the first recipes I created on my blog!

Ingredients:

1 cup of fruit (I love using berries or apples!)

2 TB chia seeds

Stevia to taste or 2-3 TB honey

Directions:

1. Blend ingredients together and let sit in the fridge for about 30 - 60 minutes until it thickens!

BODYfuel Challenge - Why not try it on some pancakes or waffles? Or french toast? Yes, please!

Another great idea is to make this into a sandwich! Try taking two rice cakes with Chia Jam, nut butter, and fresh mint on top (one of Heather's favorites!) Another option is to take two pieces of your favorite breads (don't forget carbs = energy!) and add your Chia Jam in place of jelly with your nut butter for an awesome meal.

DAY 25
GREEN SMOOTHIE

Ok, so they may not be the most appealing looking cups of goo when you're done - but adding in some greens can truly up the fuel in your daily smoothies. I like to add frozen spinach instead of ice to give my smoothies some thickness and green goodness!

Ingredients:
1 frozen banana (makes it creamy!)
Handful of fresh fruit or frozen fruit (I love berries!)
Handful of fresh spinach or about ½ cup frozen spinach (instead of ice)
1 scoop protein powder of choice
1 cup of liquid (I use liquid egg whites) or you could sub milk of choice.
Note: I use liquid egg whites (found in carton at grocery store) to add more protein especially post training or coconut/almond/whatever type of milk works too!

Directions:
1. Blend and enjoy!

This is truly the smoothie I make daily! I look forward to it after every training session to refuel the body!

BODYfuel Tip - Adding chia or flax will up the nutrients and also make it thicker!

DAY 26
DOUBLE DATE CARROT BALLS

When you make these babies, you're going to want to take them on every date you go on. Not only do dates pack a big glucose punch to fill your lovely muscles with energy, but carrots are loaded with orangey vitamins that'll have your skin glowing even if the lights are dim.

Ingredients:

1 cup soaked dates

(I soak mine in about 2 cups of water overnight in the fridge, save the liquid, & then remove the pits from the dates)

¼ cup unsweet coconut flakes

3 carrot sticks (chopped)

½ cup soaked nuts

(I used Brazil nuts - just soak overnight in enough water to cover all nuts in the fridge)

*Nuts are easier to digest when you soak them and they blend better.

Sprinkle of cinnamon, nutmeg, ginger, and cloves!

2 TB of coconut flour (helps hold together!)

Instructions:

1. Blend in a food processer until combined - if it's too dry, add some of the liquid from your soaked

dates.

2. Form your sticky dough into POWERBALLS and then roll in some more coconut before storing or eating.

These are a great pre and post workout treat! Fuel those muscles.

BODYfuel Tip - Turn your soaked dates into simple syrup. The liquid left over from your soaked dates can also be used to create a simple syrup! This is a great natural sweetener for drinks or other recipes!

BODYfuel Check - In - How did incorporating more fruits into your daily eats make you feel? What fears came up for you? How are you feeling now that you've been challenging yourself?

DAY 27
TOO HEALTHY FOR YOUR OWN GOOD?

Can you challenge yourself to add in different ingredients without feeling guilty? So often we restrict ourselves from foods because of what we see other people doing or because we feel a sense of emptiness inside. We feel like food somehow fills that emptiness, and we sometimes literally starve ourselves to feed others.

Nobody is perfect! And there is no perfect way to eat. I want to help you find a balance of enjoying all types of foods instead of going through the extremes that I went through and believing in the illusory rules I used to put in my own head.

Remember that story about how I used to freak out over eating raisins? I thought they had too much sugar and too many carbs in them. I thought I'd blow up like a balloon if I ate them. It's ironic because a week or so after that incident, a raisin truly saved my life.

Okay, so I'm being a little sarcastic in saying a raisin saved my life, but here's how it went down.

I had just finished a competition in which I had to do a pretty intense workout in a short amount of time. The competition was in the morning and I was nervous, so I hadn't eaten as much as I should have to give myself the BODYfuel I needed. When the competition was over, I felt so sick.

As I paced back and forth in the parking lot, I realized my body was shaking and I knew I needed some quick-digesting carbohydrates to give my body the energy it was asking for.

Insert raisins. Yup, those little dancing raisins came to save the day.

Once I ate some, my body instantly got the nutrients it needed and my blood sugar stabilized.

This just goes to show that our bodies are smart, people! They ask for what they need. It finally hit me square in the face: a.) I needed to listen to what my body was telling me and b.) I never really feared the raisins. I had just bought into the notion that food filled with carbs and sugars couldn't benefit me.

You have to experience things in order to really learn them, which is why I'm encouraging you to experience these recipes for yourself.

Now that you know all about my experience with raisins, let's get to the point of this section - sometimes we are "too healthy" for our own good.

I use that "healthy" word loosely here because I don't mean that taking care of yourself isn't good. But if we restrict ourselves and never allow ourselves to just eat something for pleasure or enjoyment, it affects our minds.

Ask yourself this question - are you eating for vanity or are you eating for vitality? That's a great point to make because if you're eating for vitality, you will always intuitively know what is going to serve you. But if you're eating for vanity, then you're going to feel unfulfilled and unhappy.

Healthy foods are wonderful for us, but do we really want to live our lives never enjoying chocolate, ice cream, or french fries?

It's common sense that eating ten hamburgers and ten orders of fries a day is not so great for our insides. But there is nothing wrong with enjoying this type of meal with a foundation of a well-taken-care-of and nutrient-dense-filled body.

That way, you have a stronger physical foundation to process these foods and also a stronger mental foundation to allow yourself to let go and enjoy it.

Of course, it doesn't have to be a hamburger and fries. Maybe you fear something as simple as raisins or bread. In this next series, we're going to work together to try fresh, power-packed twists on commonly decadent recipes.

CINNAMON PEAR FRENCH TOAST

For some reason, anything "bread" related went out the window in my old ways. I used to not even look down a bread aisle, fresh or frozen. Why? Well, the rules in my head said, "No bread for YOU!" But, my taste buds we're itching for some squishy goodness. With so many bread options now - you can truly find a brand or type that you may like!

Ingredients:

2 or 3 pieces of bread of your choice!

2 TB flax meal

¾ cup liquid egg whites (or 2 eggs and 1 egg white)

½ cup milk of choice (I used vanilla coconut milk)

Splash of vanilla extract

Sprinkle of cinnamon and allspice

Splash of liquid stevia (about 5 drops)

1 Pear diced, sprinkled with cinnamon

Directions:

French Toast:

1. Combine all of the ingredients (except the bread & pears) in a large enough bowl to fit the piece of bread into.

2. Once the wet mix is combined, place a piece of bread into the mix and submerge until it soaks up

some liquid.

3. Flip to the other side and let soak for a few seconds.
4. Place the piece of bread into a sprayed pan on medium heat on the stove or griddle.
5. Repeat this process with the other piece(s) of bread.
6. Cook for a few minutes on each side until browned & a bit crispy!
7. Remove from the pan, top with pears, and ENJOY!

Pears:
1. Spray a separate pan and add in your diced pears!
2. Sprinkle with cinnamon and let cook on medium heat for about 10 minutes or until cooked through.
3. Makes a great topper on your french toast!

BODYfuel Tip - I personally like my french Toast topped with some 100% pure maple syrup, but you could try coconut nectar, molasses, yogurt, nut butter, a "dippy" egg (aka sunny side up), or anything you'd like! The possibilities are pretty endless since most combos go well with french toast.

Why not add some of your homemade coconut whipped cream up on that toast? Hiyo!

BODYfuel Check - In - Do you find that it's really difficult for you to just let go, relax, and enjoy a night out to dinner without worrying about calories, how they prep the food, or sticking to a "only eating healthy" rule?

Sometimes this can make us have a fear of being social since not all of the food being cooked is "controlled" by us! This week, I challenge you to have a meal, order what you WANT (not what you think you "should" have), and write down how you feel after. Don't forget to check in with your soul sisters in the BODYpeace community!

DAYS 28 & 29
BODYfood FEAR - NIGHT TIME SNACKS

Don't eat after 7 p.m. - it'll make you gain weight!

Take a deep breath and let's chat.

One time on TV, when I was younger, I remember hearing someone say that eating ANYTHING after 7:00 p.m. will make you gain weight. Let's zone in here on that extreme word "anything."

So, if I eat a piece of spinach after 7:00 p.m...I'm going to gain weight?

Do you see how you can so easily be manipulated into believing something very extreme? Now, sometimes, for digestive reasons, some people can't eat certain things late at night - which is totally fine. You know you! I'm focusing more on the fear that any food item you put in your mouth past 7 p.m. will make you gain weight.

What I want to touch on is this restriction we put on ourselves past a certain time.

For example, some days I eat dinner at 4 p.m., then come 8 p.m., I am STARVING. Especially after a day of working, training clients, running around, and training, my body needs more fuel for that day. So, I'll have a snack.

Everyone's needs are different, and you may not have been hungry or have fueled your body enough earlier in the day. But I think it is truly important to focus not on the time we are eating, but that you can allow yourself to have a snack at night if your body is signaling to you that it's hungry and that your digestion is totally cool with it.

There are some days when your body needs another balanced meal or snack past a certain hour...and that's okay! Sometimes, your body will actually feel more rested throughout the night after having a snack before bed so that you don't wake up in the middle of the night starving.

Our bodies recover from training throughout the night, so we need that BODYfuel to help the process. And guess what? CARBS are okay at night. I used to fear eating carbs past 7 p.m., then I challenged myself to eat a snack at night that included them, and I felt so much better that night and the next day.

Am I saying it's all magic? No, but the point here is to challenge you to not live your life according to a clock. Live your life according to your body's natural hunger rhythms.

Listen to your body and its needs. If you're starving at 8 p.m., don't just sip tea and fight through your hunger pains. Let yourself listen to the cues of your body asking for more nutrients and know that it's okay to do so, again, as long as your digestion is down with it!

Some of my favorite night time snacks are usually sweet, since I do have a sweet tooth. I love making some cookies or frozen yogurt to switch it up! But these can also be eaten any time of the day.

How did you feel after eating past a certain time that may have initially made you uncomfortable?

DAY 28
CHIA CHERRY CHUNK COOKIE – FOR ONE!

Looks like we've brought chia back to the party - a party of one! Adding in some dried fruit (that used to be a no-no in my restrictive mind) and chocolate chunks will truly make these cookies a winner in your book!

Ingredients:

½ cup pumpkin puree

(can substitute banana or applesauce)

¼ cup oat flour (oats pulsed until a flour consistency)

¼ cup rolled oats (not pulsed)

1 or 2 squares of dark chocolate of choice, chopped

½ cup dried cherries

2 tsp cinnamon

10 drops of liquid stevia

1 tsp vanilla extract

¼ tsp baking powder

Directions:

1. Preheat oven to 375 degrees.

2. Combine all of the above ingredients in a bowl.

3. Put the cookie dough onto a sprayed parchment lined cookie sheet.

4. Shape into one big cookie (or multiple mini ones).

5. Bake at 375 for about 14-16 minutes or until browned.

6. Let cool and enjoy with a big glob of (unmeasured) peanut butter!

DAY 29
WE ALL SCREAM FOR...FRONANA!

Fronana is a term I coined for blending a frozen banana with any type of extra ingredients for ice cream. One of my other fears used to be having fruit before bed because I was told I'd gain weight. Whelp, I personally have enjoyed fruit with my night time snack and I honestly am okay. Again, find what works for you - but fruit shouldn't be feared. I think I'm making up for the days that I used to restrict myself from bananas - for real.

Ingredients:
1 large, frozen banana
¼ cup – ½ cup milk of choice (You want enough to blend but not too liquid-y)
2 TB chia seeds
A few drops of hazelnut stevia
A few drops of cinnamon vanilla stevia or feel free to use any type of sweetener you desire!
Sprinkle of cinnamon

BODYfuel Tip - I like to chop up fresh bananas and stick them in the freezer in a Ziploc bag.

Directions:
1. Put all ingredients into a blender and hit power -

simple as that!

2. If it's too thick, and the noise coming from your blender sounds like someone chopping down a tree, that's its way of asking for more liquid!   (Very often, my parents will yell into the kitchen, "Are you okay in there?")

3. You can either eat right away, or stick into the freezer for 10 - 20 minutes and it will firm up nicely.

I suggest topping it with raspberries, sunflower seed butter, and a few pieces of dark chocolate. YUMMM.

BODYfuel Check - In - Did eating past a certain hour make you feel anxious as if the food would be stored immediately? I used to fear this too - but once I truly challenged myself just to enjoy a snack at night if I was hungry, I began to realize that my body embraced it and loved the extra fuel for recovery!

DAY 30
WHAT THE HECK IS A POWERCAKE?

If I had a nickel for every time I was asked that question - I'd be rolling in the dough.

It's only fitting to end this thirty day BODYpeace journey with a signature recipe that started my whole website. And it's where my passion routes from.

Ever since I can remember, my family has enjoyed huge Sunday morning breakfasts together. My dad would always make pancakes before my soccer games, and my mom would always ask him, "Did you make them powercakes?" Which, essentially, was their way of sneaking healthy ingredients into our pancakes.

I didn't like eating healthy foods as a kid, and my mom always wanted to make sure that I had some form of power to give me energy to play in my soccer game! For years now I've called our pancakes, "powercakes!" Which really means, a nutrient packed pancake that gives you "power" to get through your day!

People would always ask what they were, so I'd explain to them the powercake concept. People started to ask for the recipes, so I thought starting a website would be a great way to share them. Hence how the blog started and which led me to all of you beautiful people!

BODYfuel POWERCAKE (special edition including ALL of fats, carbs, and proteins)

Ingredients:

½ cup of oats (ground into flour)

2 eggs (or flax egg of choice)

½ cup milk of choice

1 scoop of protein powder of choice

A handful of fruit of choice

Cinnamon to taste

Stevia to taste or 1 - 2 TB of sweetener (honey, maple syrup, coconut nectar)

1 tsp of baking powder

Sprinkles (YES - add all the sprinkles!) This is to celebrate your BODYpeace journey! And hey, buy some organic ones if that floats your BODYpeace boat. No judging here.

Directions:

1. Pulse your oats in a food processor or blender until flour consistency.

2. Combine oat flour, protein powder, cinnamon, sprinkles, and fruit.

3. Add in your eggs (or flax egg), milk, and stevia until a nice consistency forms.

4. If too thick, add a little more liquid until it thins out a bit!

5. Cook like pancakes on a griddle or pan at medium heat until 1 side bubbles, then flip and finish!

6. You could also throw this into the oven and make 1 big cake by cooking it at 350 degrees for about 25 minutes (or until cooked through).

7. Cut, serve, and ENJOY!

BODYfuel Check - In – Take this time to reflect on your night time snacks. Did you enjoy eating them? Did any fears come up for you eating a little later at night? How did you feel before, during, and after the meal?

Living a BODYpeace Life!

You did it! You deserve to do a celebration dance. So, go do one and then come back here to read the rest.

Welcome to your BODYpeace life. Congrats, soul sister! By now, we hope you've learned this from your BODYpeace journey: when you fall in love with your journey, the destination becomes irrelevant. What does that mean? It means that you are grateful to be here now. It means that you are no longer concerned about getting anywhere. Now that you have these tools in your tool belt, know that YOU are the teacher of your own BODYpeace journey. These are not just for us and you - these tools are yours to spread and share with everyone you know who needs them. We are so proud of you for doing this for yourself. You can go through the whole journey as many times as you need. You'll find that every time you go back and do it again, you'll receive a new insight. That is the magic of this process. There is always something new to discover about yourself.

To keep up your BODYpeace lifestyle, we suggest staying active in the BODYpeace Facebook community. You always have the support of your BODYpeace soul sisters. All of your meditations, bonuses, and goodies can always be found at http://bodypeacemovement.com/book. We have so many surprises in store for you beyond this book so keep in touch with us. Reach out to us on Twitter and Instagram at @HeatherWaxman and @KaseyArena. Tag us in all your pictures using the hashtag #BODYpeace. We absolutely love seeing your journey unfold.

We wish you a life free of shame, free of body hang-ups, and full of freedom and BODYpeace. May you be blessed, happy, and true to you. You are divinely unique and you are destined to share that with the world. Cheers to YOU, sister. Now, go spread your BODYpeace like wildfire!

About Kasey

Kasey Arena is a Certified Personal Trainer, Strength & Conditioning Coach, Corporate Fitness Professional, & has a Bachelor's Degree in Health & Physical Education. Kasey is a fitness, health, and food enthusiast and the creator and voice behind the POWERCAKES blog and website.

Kasey has a great passion and enthusiasm for fitness, fueling your body, cooking and baking. Kasey prides herself on teaching & inspiring others to find their own balance in life. Kasey stresses a personal outlook with her motto, "Be true to you!" and truly believes that you can live an abundant life in all areas as long as you stay true to yourself.

Check out Kasey at www.KaseyArena.com to join her online True To You Fitness community with weekly workouts, training tips, monthly fuel-your-body cooking videos, special discounts, group challenges, & bonus coaching.

About Heather

Heather Waxman is a spiritual lifestyle coach, author, speaker, and musician. She helps women learn how to embrace their sensitivity and stop chasing perfect. She was a meditation expert for Tone It Up's wildly successful Love Your Body series and is a monthly columnist for Over the Moon magazine. Heather, called the "Inner Peace Guru," breathes new life and an air of rawness into the spiritual conversation. Through her deeply healing and transformational meditations, vlogs, and her willingness to be open and vulnerable with her followers, Heather has created a tight-knit and loving community of soul sisters who support one another on their spiritual paths. Fun fact: If you hang out with Heather, you'll most likely see a trail of white feathers following you around (it's true!). Get some of Heather's best guided meditations by signing up for her free weekly newsletter at www.heatherwaxman.com!

Made in the USA
San Bernardino, CA
06 November 2017